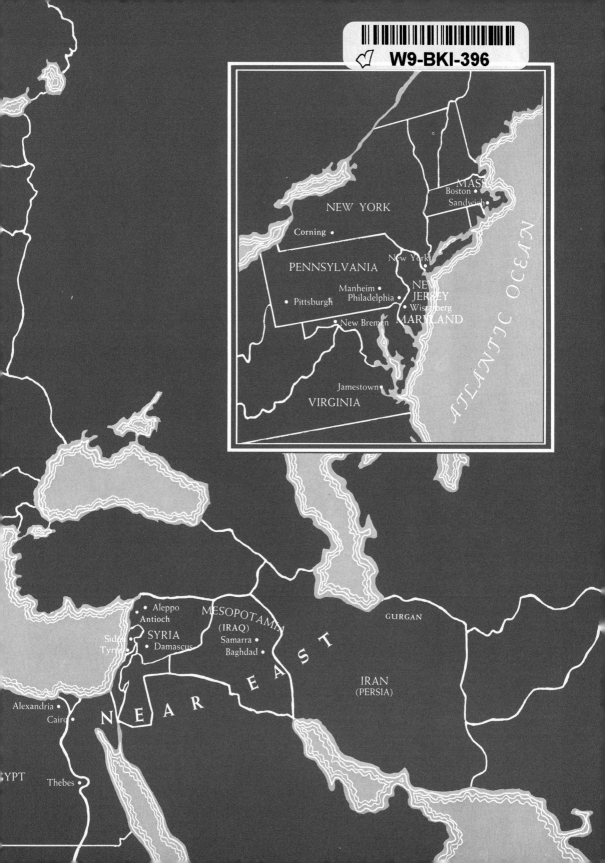

ATLANTIC OCEAN

NEW YORK

MASS.
Boston •
Sandwich •

Corning •

PENNSYLVANIA

New York •

Manheim •
Philadelphia •

NEW
JERSEY

Pittsburgh •

Wistarberg •

MARYLAND

New Bremen •

Jamestown •

VIRGINIA

N E A R   E A S T

Aleppo •
Antioch •

MESOPOTAMIA
(IRAQ)

GURGAN

Sidon •
Tyre •

SYRIA

Damascus •

Samarra •
Baghdad •

IRAN
(PERSIA)

Alexandria •

Cairo •

EGYPT

Thebes •

# GLASS

## FROM
## THE CORNING MUSEUM
## OF GLASS

## A Guide to the Collections

THE CORNING MUSEUM OF GLASS

CORNING, NEW YORK  •  1974

". . . for they shall suck of the abundance of the seas, and of treasures hid in the sand." In the Augsburg Bible of 1730 Johann Georg Pinz has illustrated this passage from Chapter 33 of the Book of Deuteronomy with an allegorical engraving of the glassmaker's trade.

COPYRIGHT 1974 THE CORNING MUSEUM OF GLASS
PRINTED IN U. S. A.
*Library of Congress Catalogue Card Number: 74-82136*

GLASS | FROM THE CORNING MUSEUM OF GLASS

# Preface

THE collections of The Corning Museum of Glass include objects from all of the historical periods in which glass has been made. The objects range from the Egyptian and Mesopotamian cored vessels of the 15th century B. C., to the creations of studio artists working in glass today. This guidebook is intended as a summary of the 13,500 objects currently in the Museum's collections and as an outline of the history connecting them.

The present edition is a revision and expansion of three previous editions which have been published since 1955. As with the others, it is a composite of contributions of many staff members of the Museum, both past and present.

ROBERT H. BRILL, *Director*
The Corning Museum of Glass

January, 1974

GLASS first appeared in the form of obsidian, a product of volcanic eruptions which occurred about forty million years ago. Where masses of silica were fused by the intense heat, a brown-black translucent glass was formed, a hard material from which simple tools and weapons could be chipped.

Man-made glass appears to have evolved from the manufacture of faience—a molded and fired mixture of crushed quartz, soda, and lime coated with an alkaline glaze and colored with metallic oxides. The production of faience started as early as the fourth millennium B.C. These ingredients subjected to sufficiently high temperature and in the presence of an excess of soda will form a true glass.

Most of the few solid glass objects made before 1500 B.C. have survived in the form of beads: simple pierced disks, cylinders, and ovoids. They were apparently built up on a removable wire and later, during the early part of the 18th Dynasty (1567-1320 B.C.), ornamented with glass thread and inlaid decoration.

Glass beads play a vital though seldom spectacular role throughout history. During several periods, particularly in East Asia, they are the only indications of glassmaking and, in the case of China, provide the earliest recognized link between glassmakers in the East and West. Glass beads have served as currency and as adornment, not only as inexpensive imitations but also as precious jewels mounted in gold.

(1) *Necklace of Glazed Ceramic and Glass Beads*
EGYPT
PROBABLY BEFORE 1500 B.C.      ACC. No. 50.1.47

9

(2) *Amphoriskos, Probably a Cosmetic Container*

EGYPT

CA. 1450-1350 B.C.

HT. 4½″ (11.5 CM.)

ACC. No. 50.1.1

THE 18th Dynasty marked the beginning of the New Empire, the third great era in ancient Egyptian history. During this period the armies of Thutmose I and his successors reunited the empire and extended its boundaries as far as the Euphrates. The death of ambitious Queen Hatshepsut placed full power in the hands of the great Pharaoh, Thutmose III, and later the fanatical Akhenaten introduced his One-God religion. To the 18th Dynasty are attributed the first vessels made entirely of glass.

These early pieces have survived in sufficiently large numbers to suggest that a well organized industry existed. They pose a problem in that they are not the crude efforts to be expected in the first glass vessels, but are products of skill and experience. However, the centuries of experience with glaze and glass-like frit and faience no doubt contributed to the apparently sudden appearance of the first glass vessels. Their form and decoration are derived from the older ceramic and lapidary arts although certain characteristics of the new medium have been incorporated in the objects, such as embedded trailings of colored glass thread. In Mesopotamia, at roughly the same period, an independent glass industry was developing. Its products were similar in form and technique to those made in Egypt, though their decoration was distinctly different in character.

(3) *Amphoriskos*

MESOPOTAMIA     HT. 4¼″ (10.8 CM.)
CA. 8TH C. B.C.     ACC. NO. 63.1.29

11

## (4) *Amphoriskos of Ivory and Red-Brown Glass*

EASTERN MEDITERRANEAN AREA

HT. 4⅞″ (12.5 CM.)

6TH-4TH C. B.C.        ACC. No. 51.1.103

Vessels resembling the small containers of the 18th Dynasty, though produced a thousand years later and excavated in large quantities, were made in the same manner as their proto-types: by covering a removable core with molten glass. Objects of this type have been excavated in widely separated areas and are most likely the product of eastern Mediterranean countries. They may have been transported filled with cosmetics by Phoe-nician ships and Syrian caravans to the capitals of the ancient world.

## (5) *Head Bead of Yellow, Black, and White Glass*

NEAR EAST        HT. 1¾″ (4.5 CM.)

PROBABLY 6TH-2ND C. B.C.        ACC. No. 53.1.2

Toward the end of the 1st millennium B.C., Alexandria was fast becoming one of the greatest cities in the ancient world. Second only to Rome, this Egyptian capital became the center of commerce between Europe and the Arabian and Indian East. Not least among the many fine craftsmen working there were the glassmakers to whose ingenuity and ability much of the finest work of the period must be credited. Among the various types of glass objects they pro-duced are a series of bead pendants modeled in the form of caricatures of the inhabitants of foreign countries.

12

## (6)  *Inlay Head*

EGYPT — HT. 8¼″ (21.0 CM.)

CA. 1000-500 B.C. — ACC. NO. 55.1.63

The manufacture of glass inlays, used to embellish mummy cases, statues, wooden thrones, ivories and jewel caskets was a major part of the early glass industry. Due to the versatile imitative qualities of glass pastes, they were given the same prominence as carnelian and turquoise. The inlays in the funerary mask of Tutankhamen, the last Pharaoh of the 18th Dynasty, and in the furnishings of his tomb are the most outstanding examples. The green color of this unusually large head, made of separate parts and itself inlaid with glass of contrasting color, is a result of the decomposition of the original red matrix.

## (7)  *Carved Vase*

PROBABLY NEAR EAST — HT. 7 9/16″ (19.2 CM.)

POSSIBLY CA. 800-600 B.C. — ACC. NO. 55.1.66

The first clear or nearly clear glass, apparently an imitation of rock crystal, seems to have been perfected by Mesopotamian glassmakers. A thick-walled vase, inscribed with the name of Sargon II (722-705 B.C.), is in the British Museum, and a fine cut bowl of clear glass has been found at Gordion, Turkey, in a late eighth century B.C. tomb. In Achaemenid Persia and later in the Hellenistic world, this transparent material remained in high fashion. Heavily carved or decorated with gold leaf, these bowls and beakers ranked with the finest luxury glass made during this period.

13

(8)  *Cameo Cup*

(Gift of Arthur A. Houghton, Jr.)

ROMAN EMPIRE                    HT. $2\frac{7}{16}''$ (6.2 CM.)

POSSIBLY 1ST C. A.D.            ACC. No. 52.1.93

THE rise of the Roman Empire witnessed a tremendous increase in manufacturing activity, comparable in a sense to the industrial revolution of the 19th century. The discovery that glass could be formed by blowing, which occurred about 50 B.C., probably in Syria, was the most important single event in the whole history of glassmaking: objects could now be made quickly with almost unlimited variations in size and shape.

Many glassblowers and decorators from Syria and Egypt, skillful descendents of old traditions, spread west and north to establish new factories. They followed the conquests of the Roman Legions and, by ship and caravan, brought their products and their craft to the remotest parts of the Empire. During four centuries, luxury vessels for temple and palace, beads for adornment or trade, and utilitarian vessels for house and market were made in large quantities.

Together with quantity came new standards of quality, and high among the achievements of the great glassmakers of this period is a small group of vessels known as glass cameos. These cameos were most frequently made by covering or casing a matrix of blue glass with a layer of translucent white glass which was then carved with ornamental designs or scenes of mythological or genre character. The variable thickness of the white layer produced subtle tonal variations. The cup illustrated here, unusual for its fine condition, bears a mythological scene devoted to the worship of Priapus, a fertility god.

(9) *Fragment of Cameo Glass in Six Layers*

ROMAN EMPIRE          HT. $2\frac{5}{16}''$ (5.9 CM.)

1ST C. A.D.          ACC. No. 62.1.24

## (10)  *Molded and Cut Bowl*

MESOPOTAMIA    HT. 2½″ (6.4 CM.)
CA. 3RD C. B.C.    ACC. No. 62.1.21

In the centuries immediately preceding the discovery of the blowpipe,
a substantial number of bowls were
made by molding. The glass was
generally rather thick, often very
clear and decorated with wheel-cut
designs similar to those used on their
precious silver prototypes. This early
Mesopotamian glass industry established traditions which lived on into
the Sasanian and later Islamic
periods.

## (11)  *Fused Mosaic Plaque*

PROBABLY ALEXANDRIA    L. 1⅝″ (2.8 CM.)
1ST C. B.C.—1ST C. A.D.    ACC. No. 59.1.95

Of the great ancient schools of glassmaking,
the Alexandrian is distinguished by the
emphasis placed on luxurious colors and
textures. The basis of one series of techniques was mosaic inlays of glass of different
colors and degrees of transparency. Many
fine fragments have survived to prove the
existence of mosaic plates made entirely of
glass flowers complete with intricate blos-
soms, leaves, and stems. Intricate portrait
heads such as this were used for inlay purposes. Larger compositions in the same
basic technique were employed as wall
coverings.

16

## (12)  *Mold-Blown Ewer*

PROBABLY SIDON          HT. 9¼″ (23.5 CM.)
1ST C. A.D.               ACC. NO. 59.1.76

Centuries before the beginning of our era
the eastern coast of the Mediterranean
became an important center for the early
glass industry. During the Roman Empire
this area continued to lead in producing
glass vessels in large quantities and of superior quality. Glass factories seem to have
been concentrated around the towns of
Sidon and Tyre. The glassmaker Ennion,
one of the first to have signed his products,
appears to have operated a factory on the
Syrian coast before moving to the Roman
peninsula.

## (13)  *The Paris Plate*

POSSIBLY SYRIA, ANTIOCH  D. 8¼″ (21.0 CM.)
CA. 250-350 A.D.          ACC. NO. 55.1.85

When Rome was at the height of her power,
the villas of the rich throughout the Empire
were sumptuously decorated with colorful
frescoes and marble statues; the wealthy
drank from golden cups and precious glass
vessels. This shallow bowl of thin clear
glass is decorated with a scene painted in
several colors depicting the Judgment of
Paris, the event which culminated in the
abduction of the Greek princess, Helen, and
the ensuing Trojan war.

17

(14)  *The Daphne Ewer*

POSSIBLY SYRIA, ANTIOCH        HT. 8¾″ (22.2 CM.)

CA. LATE 2ND-EARLY 3RD C. A.D.        ACC. NO. 55.1.86

Dᴜʀɪɴɢ the early Roman Empire the arts and crafts kept pace with the political and economic development. Accompanying the Roman soldiers on their expeditions, Oriental merchants and Jewish artisans established themselves in Gaul and the Rhineland to continue their trades. They lived comfortably in newly founded towns, protected by strong garrisons and stimulated by native markets. Indigenous factories were started where the foreigners from the East taught Gallic and Germanic peoples how to blow, shape, and decorate glass. Such a factory, for instance, was owned in Gaul by a certain Frontinus who put his name on the bases of barrel-shaped bottles. Other glass houses, concentrated around Cologne, specialized in snake-thread decorated vessels or made wares for the diamond-point engraver. Small shops were put up where strange stuffs and glimmering metal work could be purchased or in which highly skilled craftsmen turned out master works of glass like the famous undercut diatreta vessels.

The primary source of inspiration for glassblowers and decorators alike throughout the Empire seems to have been the country where glassblowing originated: the province of Syria and neighboring lands. Antioch on the Orontes was a metropolis and center of culture and wealth for many hundreds of years within this area. The Daphne ewer, an opaque white glass ewer with rich cold-painted and gilded decoration might have been made there in a shop devoted to the manufacture of luxurious artifacts. The scene depicts the story of Daphne who was turned by her protecting father into a tree when the pursuing, love-mad Apollo tried to touch her. An inscription on the shoulder of the ewer says "The Beautiful," referring to the lovely Daphne.

19

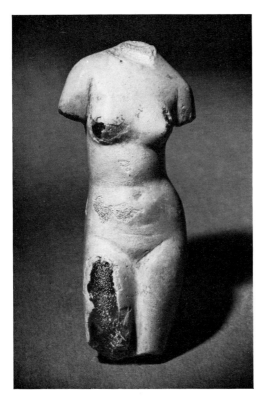

(15) *Torso of Aphrodite*

PROBABLY NEAR EAST OR ITALY

HT. 3¾″ (9.5 CM.)

CA. 1ST-2ND C. A.D.      ACC. NO. 55.1.84

This torso of Aphrodite in greenish glass was undoubtedly copied from a Greek statue in marble. A similar glass sculpture is in the Museum of Fine Arts, Boston. It was molded in separate parts, probably by the lost wax process, but only the torso survived. The smooth, yellowish layer covering most of the surface is the result of decomposition caused by chemical reactions during its long burial.

(16) *Chalice*

ROMAN EMPIRE      HT. 5⅝″ (14.3 CM.)

CA. 1ST C. A.D.      ACC. NO. 64.1.3

Under Caesar and his successors, glassmaking developed into an empire-wide industry; glass ewers and bottles excavated as far north as England and as far west as Spain are often indistinguishable from similar pieces excavated in Syria and Rome. Variety in function and form grew accordingly, not only in the production of utilitarian vessels but in all types of luxury and commemorative glasses. This chalice of amber-colored glass with spattered colored flecks is a good example of an elegant glass of a type found in the ruins of Pompeii.

20

## (17)  *The Oedenburg Gladiator Beaker*

*Signed: M. Licinius Diceus F(ecit)*

(Gift of Arthur A. Houghton, Jr.)

WESTERN EUROPE (FOUND AT OEDENBURG, HUNGARY)
CA. 50-100 A.D.   HT. 3¾″ (9.5 CM.)   ACC. NO. 57.1.4

Almost parallel in time to the invention of the blow-pipe was the discovery and subsequent wide use of molds incised with decorative motifs or narrative themes. They were made of a ceramic material, generally in two parts and probably hinged together. A gather of glass, inflated into such a mold, received the impression of the pattern on its exterior. This method insured quick, precise, and uniform shaping with the additional advantage of simultaneously decorating any type of vessel. This cup, commemorating two gladiatorial combats, is unique as it bears the signature of the maker: the name M. Licinius Diceus appears in large letters on the shoulder.

## (18)  *Ewer*

SYRIA                 HT. 16½″ (42.0 CM.)
2ND-3RD C. A.D.           ACC. NO. 64.1.18

The years immediately following the discovery of glassblowing witnessed many new developments in glassmaking and in the usages of glass. Virtually all the decorative techniques known today, with the exception of those relying on acid and heat treatment, were known to the Romans. Glassmakers traveled extensively, and there was little delay between the introduction of a new idea and its application hundreds of miles away. The nipt-diamond-ways decoration of this ewer is found almost simultaneously on objects made in Egypt and in the Rhineland. It is the first occurrence of a motif which is reused throughout the later history of glass.

21

## (19) *Engraved Bowl, Inscribed* "*Vita Bona Fruamur Felices*" (*We fortunates enjoy the good life*)

ROMAN EMPIRE      HT. 3¼″ (8.3 CM.)
PROBABLY 3RD C. A.D.     ACC. NO. 55.1.1

Of the various ways in which glass can be decorated, engraving is among the oldest. This technique was employed on an 18th Dynasty Egyptian goblet in the Metropolitan Museum of Art to depict the cartouche of Thutmose III. Later glass was actually carved in relief and intaglio. The hunting scene on this bowl is not unlike the vigorous scratch decoration employed by Rhenish glassmakers, primitive however in comparison with the superbly modeled and detailed work created two centuries earlier in Rome and Alexandria.

## (20) *The Populonia Bottle*

ROMAN        HT. 7¼″ (18.4 CM.)
4TH C. A.D.       ACC. NO. 62.1.31

Glass engraving became a popular means of decoration toward the end of the Roman Empire: hunting scenes and early Christian subjects were the most common. A few examples remain depicting cities or ancient harbors. This bottle, which was discovered in 1810, was once in the collection of Elise Bonaparte, Napoleon's sister. It depicts a view of the harbor of Puteoli, near Naples.

## (21) *Beaker*

RHINELAND        HT. 7″ (17.8 CM.)

2ND-3RD C. A.D.        ACC. NO. 62.1.15

Glassmakers in the Roman colonies became increasingly independent as the central power in Rome weakened. Although the forms and styles developed in Syria and Alexandria became more and more remote to the northern glassmakers of the Rhineland, the pincered thread of glass trailed and wound about in a snake-like design was common to both areas. Similar crimped trailings band the German *Passglas* and the *Roemer* more than a thousand years later.

## (22) *Gold Glass—"The Good Shepherd"*

PROBABLY ROME        D. 3⅞″ (9.8 CM.)

EARLY 4TH C. A.D.        ACC. NO. 66.1.37

The technique of laminating gold leaf between two pieces of glass was known as early as the 3rd century B.C. During the Roman Empire this type of decoration was used in jewelry and pendants, but more frequently appears in the bottoms of bowls and drinking vessels. Most of the surviving specimens are jagged-edged discs which appear to have been intentionally broken away from the body of vessels. Among the subjects depicted in this technique are themes from the Old and New Testaments, pagan mythology, portraits, and genre scenes.

23

## (23) *Giant Unguentarium*

NEAR EAST           HT. 15¼″ (38.8 CM.)
PROBABLY 4TH-6TH C. A.D.       ACC. NO. 54.1.100

Among the variety of objects made during the Roman Empire
are a series of small vials formed by folding one or more tubes of
glass in half. As the Roman period drew to a close, these vessels
became increasingly elaborate with complicated handles and
bands of pincered rigaree. The example pictured here is unusually
large and, with its profusion of thread decoration, not unlike the
flasks and bottles of the early Islamic period.

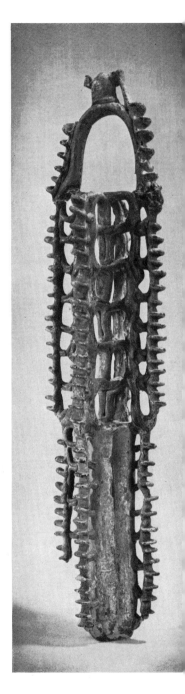

## (24) *Grotesque Head Flask*

PROBABLY RHINELAND       HT. 6 3/16″ (15.7 CM.)
3RD-4TH C. A.D.           ACC. NO. 54.1.86

Mold-blown glass was extremely
popular during the Roman Empire; in fact the rapid and successful expansion of the industry during the first century A.D. was, in
part, dependent on the development of the use of molds. Originally found among the "Sidonian-
type" bottles and jars bearing
Jewish symbols, this technique
made it possible to give a vessel
the shape of grapes or dates, fish
or apes, barrels or human heads.
Of this latter group, the double-
faced Janus head flasks originated
probably in the East, while gro-
tesque heads with accentuated
features, characterizing a foreign
race, have been found largely in
Western Europe.

24

## (25) *Cone Beaker*

RHINELAND, BELGIUM, OR NORTHERN FRANCE

HT. 9¼″ (23.5 CM.)

EARLY 6TH C. A.D.  ACC. NO. 66.1.247

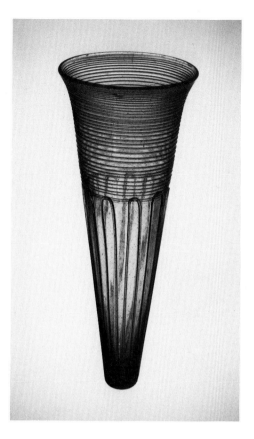

The decline of the Roman Empire affected the whole social, economic, and cultural life of the ancient world. Lavishly decorated glass bowls and ewers were no longer in demand. Mass-producing factories had to close down as markets diminished, upset by political unrest and frequent invasions. Glass vessels of the Frankish or Merovingian period have, however, survived in sufficient numbers to give us an idea of the quantity and quality of glass production. The innumerable variety of shapes and decorative motifs of the Roman period was reduced to a few distinct types. The proficiency of the craftsmen is apparent in objects like the beakers with elephant-trunk-like applications and this cone beaker.

## (26) *Bottle*

SASANIAN (PERSIA)  HT. 8″ (20.3 CM.)

6TH-7TH C. A.D.  ACC. NO. 62.1.4

A tradition of massive casting and cutting survived in Persia for over a millennium. This bottle is the linear descendent of the unique example, over 1000 years older, bearing the seal of Sargon II and now in the British Museum. Until recent years little was known of glassmaking in Sasanian Persia.

(27)  *Cut Bottle*

PROBABLY PERSIA     HT. 10¾″ (27.3 CM.)

PROBABLY 11TH C.     ACC. No. 53.1.8

MOHAMMED's flight from Mecca to Medina in 622 A.D. marks the beginning of the Islamic Era. Little more than a century after the death of Allah's Prophet, the tribes of Arabia had grown into a world power controlling an enormous empire which stretched from the Atlantic Ocean east to the borders of China. In exchange for the tolerant domination of the Islamic faith, the cultural traditions of the conquered nations were gradually absorbed into the new Empire. Under the rule of the various Caliphates representing the prophet, the arts of Egypt, Persia, Mesopotamia, and Syria contributed much to the evolution of a distinctly Islamic style.

Based primarily on the artistic forms inherited from Byzantium and Sasanian Persia, the art of Islam has undergone many changes in its thirteen centuries of existence. If the Islamic style has one dominant characteristic, it might be defined as the subordination of the individual motif to the general decorative effect. As symbols, flowers, animals, or figures are arranged in intricate patterns, they become stylized, and emphasis is placed on rhythmic repetition.

The Islamic style is well represented by a group of carved and engraved rock crystal and glass vessels made between the 8th and 12th centuries. Several of these have been preserved since the Middle Ages in the treasuries of European cathedrals, the richest collection being in the Treasury of the Cathedral of San Marco in Venice.

## (28) Bottle

PERSIA, ISLAMIC      HT. 6¼" (15.5 CM.)
9TH-10TH C.      ACC. No. 73.1.3

Roman influence in glassmaking gradually declined after the fall of the Empire in the West. Following the Moslem conquests in the 7th century A.D., Islamic influences became predominant in glassmaking. Shapes produced by Islamic glassmakers bear little resemblance to Roman forms. In the early period, they were decorated principally by pattern molding and pincering. By the 9th century, Islamic glassmakers had carried Sasanian techniques to new heights. Cutting and engraving the surface of the vessel was most popular. This bottle of almost colorless glass combines geometric cutting around the neck with engraved figural scenes on the body.

## (29) Hedwig Beaker

ISLAMIC      HT. 3⅜" (8.6 CM.)
12TH C.      ACC. No. 67.1.11

Literary sources of the Middle Ages confirm our belief that vessels of transparent stone and glass were thought to be as valuable as gold and silver. According to Chinese annals, the costly tributes presented by embassies to the Chinese Court in the 6th and 7th centuries included objects of glass. Al-Maqrizi, the well known Moslem historian, lists innumerable rock crystal and crystal clear glass bottles and beakers, both plain and carved, which formed a major part of the legendary rich Fatimid treasures, carried off by Turkish mercenary troops in the 11th century.

28

## (30) *Fluted Bowl*

NEAR EAST, POSSIBLY PERSIA
D. 6⅞″ (17.5 CM.)
CA. 9TH-10TH C.
ACC. No. 55.1.136

The imitative qualities of glass which made it a substitute for precious and therefore more costly stones is well exemplified by many Islamic carved objects. A turquoise-blue bowl, similar in shape to the green one illustrated here, was inscribed with the word: "Khurasan," the name of a province in eastern Persia famous for its turquoise mines. Mounted in gold, it was presented by the Shah of Persia to the Venetian Signoria in 1472 as a stately gift. As the bowl was given four centuries after it was made, both giver and receiver probably did not realize that the object's inscription had deceived them: the bowl was made of glass in perfect imitation of turquoise.

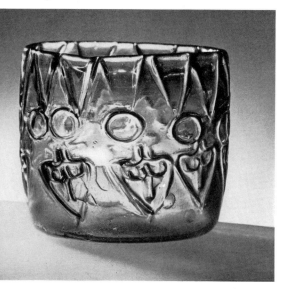

## (31) *Free-Blown Cup with Impressed Decoration*

NEAR EAST              HT. 3 3/16″ (8.0 CM.)
8TH-9TH C.             ACC. No. 55.1.17

The palmette is particularly important among the motifs inherited by the Islamic style from Sasanian prototypes. This leaf-like device had many variations and eventually developed into the most common of all Islamic motifs, the *arabesque*. A band of heart-shaped palmettes has been impressed on this cup with a pair of pincers in which the design has been carved, a technical device apparently of Islamic origin.

(32) *Cut Cup*

PROBABLY PERSIA          D. 5½″ (14.0 CM.)

PROBABLY 9TH C.          ACC. No. 53.1.109

Ever since the discovery of the blowpipe, glassmakers have striven to obtain clear glass with the same clarity and brilliance as rock crystal. Though their formulas produced a far less brilliant product, the craftsmen of the Near East cut and engraved a great number of glass objects with the same techniques and designs as were used on the more precious rock crystal. These objects, produced mainly between the 9th and 11th centuries, present a homogeneous stylistic development and, in quality, can be ranked with the enameled works of the 13th and 14th centuries. The cup illustrated here probably dates from the beginning of this development. Animal motifs constituted a large part of the vocabulary of pre-Islamic artists, though the once powerful symbolism appears to have been lost. Four birds alternating with four ibexes are carved in high relief on the wall of the cup, and a stylized "tree" guarded by falcons decorates the bottom. This vessel, broken and heavily weathered, represents an achievement of considerable artistic importance. The arrangement and treatment of the various decorative elements are so closely integrated with the form of the cup that each reinforces the other, form and decoration becoming inseparable.

31

(33)  *Enameled Mosque Lamp*

SYRIA, DAMASCUS (?)     HT. 12″ (30.5 CM.)

CA. 1350     ACC. NO. 52.1.86

THE richly gilded and enameled glasses of the 12th, 13th, and 14th centuries are among the greatest of the many Islamic contributions to the art of glassmaking. Although the earlier Fatimid traditions of lustreware are prominent among the stylistic sources of this remarkable group, Syria, particularly Damascus and Aleppo, deserves credit for the perfection of the enameling and gilding techniques. Many magnificently embellished vessels now in the possession of European cathedrals and museums were brought back by the returning Crusaders.

Of the several shapes on which this type of decoration was applied, the mosque lamp form has survived in greatest number. Made for the Mameluke Sultans and their Emirs, they frequently bear the name or personal symbol of the donor, together with an inscription from the Koran. These lamps were designed to be hung from the ceilings of mosques by chains attached to the handles.

Of primary importance to the stylistic development of Arabic enameling was the introduction by the Mongols of Chinese decorative elements. First evident on lamps of the late 13th century, this influence was most strongly felt during the 14th; the lamp reproduced here, with its natural floral motifs and particular style of drawing, is characteristic of the later period.

33

## (34) *Double Unguentarium*

NEAR EASTERN, POSSIBLY SYRIA

HT. $4\frac{7}{16}''$ (11.3 CM.)

6TH-8TH C.            ACC. No. 55.1.109

During the entire history of glass, glassmakers
have displayed their virtuosity by creating
*tours de force* which often negated the original
practical purpose of the shape they had set out
to make. Islamic craftsmen were particularly
prone to such flamboyant displays. This fanciful form, a trail-decorated double unguentarium carried by two horses, is a typical
example of this period.

## (35) *Enameled and Gilded Vase*

SYRIA, PROBABLY DAMASCUS

OR ALEPPO            HT. $11\frac{7}{8}''$ (30.2 CM.)

CA. 1320-30            ACC. No. 55.1.36

Apart from the well-known lamps which
adorned Moslem holy places, the Syrian
enamelers decorated a wide variety of
footed bowls, globes, sprinklers, fragile
beakers, and long necked bottles. The vase
illustrated is covered with golden arabesques
and fish motifs finely outlined in red. The
inscription, repeating the word: "The
Wise," refers to the God of Mohammed.
The medallions on the neck probably contain the armorial symbol of the nobleman
who commissioned this object.

34

## (36) *Enameled Beaker*

VENICE           HT. $3\frac{15}{16}''$ (10.0 CM.)
PROBABLY LATE 15TH C.      ACC. NO. 55.3.12

The beginning of enameled glass in Europe is an out-
growth of the economic and cultural ties established
in the late Middle Ages between the Near East and
Venice, the maritime center of the West. While the
magnificence of captured treasures and the skill of
Syrian craftsmen stimulated the art of glassmaking in
Venice before 1400 A.D., there was a reverse movement after the sack of Damascus. Henceforth, Murano-
made glass, ordered by Oriental potentates, was shipped
to the East. This beaker, so similar in style and decoration to Venetian work, was found in Damascus. Its
weathered surface resembles that of Islamic glass excavated in the Near East, but it is most likely a Venetian export.

## (37) *Nativity Medallion*

WESTERN EUROPE OR BYZANTIUM
         D. (MAX. AX.) $1\frac{3}{16}''$ (3.0 CM.)
PROBABLY 12TH-13TH C.    ACC. NO. 53.3.18

The use of glass to simulate semi-precious
stones goes back to antiquity. The early
Egyptian glazed necklace (figure 1) is clearly an attempt to imitate more precious materials, and later, during the Middle Ages,
glass pastes were used side by side with
precious stones and cameos, often as part of
the elaborate decoration of liturgical vest-
ments. The Nativity represented here is con-
sistent with the medieval interpretation in
which the humble manger prefigures the
final sacrifice, the crib being placed as an
altar in the center of the composition.

35

(38)  *Enameled Goblet*

VENICE

1ST QUARTER 16TH C.

HT. $9\frac{5}{16}''$ (23.6 CM.)

ACC. NO. 53.3.38

WHILE new traditions developed in the Near East after the decline of Rome, the art of glassmaking in the West was all but lost. A few isolated glasshouses continued to produce, but their products were few and, compared to previous achievements, extremely crude. The monumental works of the stained glass makers of the Middle Ages are great and notable contributions in an otherwise primitive and rather unproductive glassmaking period.

Toward the middle of the 11th century, there is evidence that glassmakers were brought to Venice from Constantinople to produce mosaics for the Basilica of S. Marco. By the 13th century the industry was well established and a guild was formed. The ever increasing number of glasshouses and the danger of fire led to an edict in 1291 transferring all glassmaking operations to the neighboring island of Murano. There large scale production could be pursued without endangering the city, and new techniques and formulas could be developed in relative secrecy. The elegant vessels made at Murano were exported throughout Europe, and those craftsmen who ignored the threat of reprisals and fled from Murano to other countries received rich rewards for their daring and enterprise.

The wealth of the "Queen of the Adriatic" is reflected in the elaborate forms and the elegant decoration of her products. Enameling, which was practiced with consummate skill in the Near East, became one of the most successful mediums for the Venetian craftsmen of the late 15th century. Many fine examples have survived bearing allegorical and genre scenes, portraits, and other symbols.

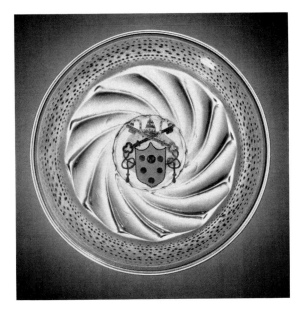

### (39)  *Plate*

VENICE               D. 9⅞″ (25.0 CM.)

1513-34             ACC. No. 57.3.44

Very little is known about the early history of glassmaking in Venice. While documentary evidence indicates a highly productive community as early as the 12th century, actual glass vessels cannot be accurately dated before the second half of the 15th century. These early vessels of deep red, blue, or green glass are heavily enameled and gilded. Frequently, armorial devices were placed at the center of plates, as in this example which bears the coat of arms of a Medici Pope.

### (40)  *Tazza with Diamond-Point Engraving*

VENICE               D. 12¼″ (31.1 CM.)

PROBABLY EARLY 17TH C.        ACC. No. 51.3.239

The Venetian love for opulence is quite apparent in paintings of the 15th and 16th centuries. Among the infinite variety of luxurious paraphenalia depicted by Venetian artists are fragile objects of glass, which were either covered with polychrome and gilded patterns or engraved with the point of a sharp instrument, usually a diamond.

The engraved floral pattern on the tazza forms an over-all lacelike texture, elegant in spite of the somewhat primitive character of the drawing

## (41) *Goblet*

VENICE OR FRANCE
HT. 6 11/16″ (17.0 CM.)
EARLY 16TH C.
ACC. No. 56.3.109

The clear *cristallo* which spread the fame of Venetian glass throughout Europe was a hard, brittle material made more transparent by the use of decolorizers which counteracted the effects of impurities in the raw materials. The properties and method of manufacture of *cristallo* were set down by Antonio Neri who wrote in 1612 his *L'Arte Vetraria*, the first book on the art of glassmaking. Made available by translations to glassmakers throughout Europe, this small volume not only contained the formulas for this material but for a great variety of other clear and colored glasses. It is quite possible that the final development in Germany of a good red glass and the perfection of glass of lead in England are the flowerings of seeds contained in this original treatise.

## (42) *Dragon-Stemmed Goblet*

VENICE
LATE 16TH C.
HT. 10¼″ (26.0 CM.)
ACC. No. 51.3.118

The dragon motif occurs constantly in the decorative arts of the Renaissance. The fantastic character of the subject was naturally a favorite for Venetian artists familiar with countless representations of St. George and the dragon. They were also frequently exposed to oriental importations and to the tales of travelers returning from the Far East where the dragon was considered sacred.

**(43)** *Covered Dragon-Stemmed Goblet*

VENICE        HT. 14″ (35.6 CM.)

16TH C.        ACC. NO. 51.3.115

**D**URING the 16th and 17th centuries, Venice was the supreme source of fine glass, supplying the tables of the wealthy throughout Europe. The income realized was an important asset to the economy of the Republic and undoubtedly a source of envy to other nations. As a monopoly, glassmaking was subject to protective legislation which sentenced to death those glassmakers who jeopardized the industry by attempting to emigrate.

Though following the technical traditions developed during the Roman period and perfected during the reign of the Mameluke Sultans, the Venetian craftsmen evolved a style entirely original and intimately in accord with the aesthetic aspirations of their leading artists.

The application of glass threads as a decorative device had been employed since antiquity, often as a mere complex of fragile forms with no obvious purpose. The 16th century Venetians on the contrary, taking advantage of the ductility of their *cristallo*, used threading as a structural material as the very basis of many designs. The swirling forms built of glass led the eye around the object, linking the parts in a fully three-dimensional whole characteristic of the late Renaissance.

The exuberant virtuosity of the glassmakers is seldom more evident than in the treatment of the snake or dragon motif. The flowing, upward movement of the spiral, echoed in the multicolored thread imbedded in the glass, is reminiscent of the contemporary achievements of Tintoretto and Giovanni da Bologna.

41

## (44) *Covered Goblet*

(Gift of Edwin J. Beinecke)

PROBABLY SOUTH GERMANY  HT. 17¾″ (45.0 CM.)

DATED 1617  ACC. No. 60.3.83

Venetian glassmaking traditions predominated throughout Europe during the 16th and 17th centuries. Spain, France, Germany, the Netherlands, even England produced glass in the Venetian style, often so successfully that the copy and the original are indistinguishable. Gridolphi, a Venetian glassmaker working in the Netherlands under the exclusive patronage of the Infanta Isabella, complained in 1607 that merchants were bringing in imitation Venetian glass which could not be distinguished from the original.

## (45) *Covered Goblet*

AUSTRIA, INNSBRUCK  HT. 12 9/16″ (31.9 CM.)

CA. 1580  ACC. No. 68.3.21

The glasshouse established in Innsbruck by Archduke Ferdinand II, which operated from about 1570 to 1590, was one of a number of Northern factories producing glass in the Venetian style (*Façon de Venise*). This covered goblet of dark *cristallo*, decorated with diamond-point engraving and gilding, is characteristic of the work of this factory. Although this glass, and others produced in Northern glasshouses, possesses all of the elements of glass made in Venice—mold-blown stem, fragility and lightness, diamond-point engraving—it has a distinct character of its own.

42

### (46) *Engraved Venetian-Style Goblet*

| | |
|---|---|
| NETHERLANDS | HT. 7⅛″ (18.1 CM.) |
| LATE 17TH C. | ACC. No. 51.3.116 |

Of the several decorative techniques employed by Venetian glassmakers, diamond-point engraving found particular favor in the Netherlands. The ornamental scratched designs which encircled many a Muranese goblet with flowers, initials, and armorial symbols were replaced by Northern engravers with lively figures and graceful calligraphy. The appearance of a typically Dutch peasant scene on a Venetian inspired goblet is interesting in that it shows a Northern penchant for Venetian glass forms as a vehicle for their own style of engraving.

### (47) *Holy Water Font*

| | |
|---|---|
| PERHAPS BELGIUM, LIEGE | HT. 9⅞″ (25.0 CM.) |
| 17TH C. | ACC. No. 51.3.199 |

The trapping of a colored spiral in a glass rod was apparently a Venetian invention, closely related to the popular white striped *filigree* glass and the prototype of the finely developed English opaque twist stem. This device was extensively used to support the bowls of Netherlandish drinking vessels. In the object reproduced here, such a rod has been twisted into an intricate pattern supporting a mold-blown holy water container.

43

(48)  *Covered Filigree Goblet-Vase*

PROBABLY VENICE             HT. 13″ (33.0 CM.)
LATE 16TH-EARLY 17TH C.     ACC. NO. 54.3.14

THE perfection and continuous popularity of the filigree technique is appropriate evidence of the genius of the 16th century Venetian glass industry. Requiring masterly craftsmanship in its execution, this lacelike glass has challenged the abilities of glassmakers in almost every glassmaking community, and it has survived to be incorporated in the simple shapes dictated by our contemporary taste.

Filigree differs from the much older technique of applying glass threads as used, for example, on the Egyptian amphoriskos reproduced in figure 2, in that a gather of glass is brought to the threading rather than vice versa. A series of straight rods or canes of white glass are placed vertically at regular intervals around the interior wall of a mold. A gather of clear glass forced into the mold picks up the canes, which fuse to the clear glass core. After re-heating and imbedding the canes by marvering, a second gather of clear glass is made over the first. This is then rolled on the marver to make it symmetrical, and it is then pulled out and twisted so that the enclosed white canes form a spiral around the clear core. If these new canes are alternated with the solid white ones in a mold and are picked up on the surface of a partially inflated gather of glass which is then expanded and shaped, a vessel of lacelike texture will eventually be formed. A particularly intricate variant of this technique entraps bubbles between the crossed canes. It is called *vetro di trina*.

(49)  *Filigree Tazza*

VENICE    HT. 5⅜″ (13.6 CM.)
16TH C.    ACC. No. 51.3.119

## (50)  *Càntir*

SPAIN, CATALONIA        HT. 16 1/16″ (40.8 CM.)
18TH C.        ACC. No. 54.3.143

Though subject to Moorish influence, Spanish glass is
notable for the inclusion of several distinctly national
forms such as the *cantir*, *porró*, and *almorrata*. The
imaginatively decorated vessel reproduced here is a
cantir, the communal drinking vessel designed to supply
a thin stream of beverage into the mouth of the drinker
without physical contact. Despite the crudity of this
attempt at filigree decoration, it is further evidence of
the far-reaching influence of Venice.

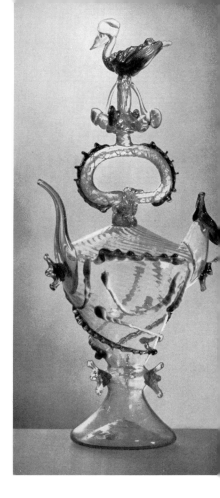

## (51)  *Candlestick*

SPAIN        HT. 6 11/16″ (17.0 CM.)
17TH-18TH C.        ACC. No. 55.3.23

Spain is unusual among European glassmaking countries in that she was subjected to a long
period of direct Mohammedan influence. Inheriting the Eastern attraction for elaborate thread

decoration, the glasshouses of
southern Spain kept Islamic traditions alive well into the 18th
century. This candlestick of milk
glass has a pattern-molded shaft
and imaginatively conceived
thread handles, results of the same
decorative fantasy that stimulated the maker of the giant late
Roman unguentarium (figure 23).

46

## (52) *Glass Thread Medallion*

PROBABLY FRANCE, NEVERS

D. (MAX. AX.) 2⅜" (6.0 CM.)

17TH C.                    ACC. NO. 53.3.34

Unlike the glassmakers of Venice, those of the equally old Italian community in Altare were migrants, some settling in France in the town of Nevers. Although what is known of their work in the Venetian style is inferior to the Dutch and German versions, the Nevers workmen were responsible for a charming group of plaquettes and figurines composed of colored glass threads. These were formed by manipulating remelted rods of glass, a technique known today as lampworking.

## (53) *Painted Bowl*

FRANCE OR NETHERLANDS

D. 14½" (36.9 CM.)

18TH C.                    ACC. NO. 53.3.27

Of the many ways in which glass vessels have been embellished with polychrome enamel and paint, few take better advantage of the refractive properties of glass than the reverse picture. As in the bowl illustrated here, the subject is seen through the glass, and so the highlights are painted first and the background last. Although the use of paint rather than fired enamel allows the artist greater flexibility in selecting and blending his colors, it has the disadvantage of being extremely fragile.

(54)  *Sepia-Enameled Roemer*

NETHERLANDS

17TH C.

HT. $4\frac{15}{16}''$ (12.5 CM.)

ACC. No. 50.3.113

ROMAN glassmaking techniques, established in northern Europe during the first centuries of our era, persisted after the decline of the Empire. By the 9th century, the Church, with the assistance of the Emperor Charlemagne, had done away with pagan burial customs, and consequently little medieval glass is to be found in graves. However, it is known that glasshouses in Hesse and the southern part of Germany were producing utilitarian vessels of simple shape as early as the 13th century. These houses were located in the forests in the midst of their fuel and ash supply, and the glass they produced is known as *Wald* or "forest" glass. As the raw materials available contained many impurities, especially iron, the resulting glass was characteristically green in color. Although some examples of *Waldglas*, dating from the 14th century, have been found as far south as Spain, the greatest output of this type was in the North and did not begin until late in the 15th century. Generally the vessels were simple, sturdy, and frequently rather primitive in execution. The most popular form was the *Roemer*, a glass of capacious size which evolved from the earlier *Nuppenbecher* form. The decoration on *Waldglas* vessels is usually confined to pads and prunts of glass applied to the stem, but the high position of the *Roemer* in the society it served is well illustrated by the frequent use of diamond-point engraving, and, more rarely, of enameling, often applied with considerable refinement and devoted to such sophisticated subjects as coats of arms and allegories.

The *Roemer* illustrated here is decorated with near-transparent sepia enameling, showing the god Mercury discovering the young Bacchus, god of wine.

GERMANY                                    HT. CA. 3″ (7.6 CM.)

15TH-16TH C.                               ACC. No. 50.3.38

Unlike the imaginative and fanciful work from
Venice, German *Waldglas* is generally confined to
a few basic forms. Among these is the *Nuppenbecher* which is nothing more than a small hipped
beaker, decorated with thorn-like prunts and supported on a tooled foot. From the number of surviving specimens, it appears to have been a popular drinking vessel, possibly derived from prunted beakers made during the 11th and 12th centuries in the Near East. Its frequent use as a
reliquary, sealed with wax, attests that this type
of glass vessel was held in high esteem by the
Church authorities.

(56)  *Beaker with Looped Prunts*

GERMANY              HT. 7$\frac{15}{16}$″ (20.2 CM.)

PROBABLY 16TH C.       ACC. No. 53.3.2

In 1564 Mathesius, a German minister,
published a collection of sermons, one
of which was devoted to the art of
glassmaking. Speaking of prunted
beakers he says: "Nowadays one applies
buttons, prunts, and rings to the glasses
to make them sturdier. Thus they can
be held more easily in the hands of
drunken and clumsy people. This is the
reason why these rigid, bumpy vessels
are favored by so many."

## (57) *Roemer*

NETHERLANDS OR GERMANY     HT. $10\frac{15}{16}''$ (27.8 CM.)

CA. 1610             ACC. No. 64.3.92

The term *Roemer* may be derived from "Roman," a term long familiar to Western people as their early history was so closely associated with the Roman Empire. Another explanation is to link the name with the Dutch word *roemen*, to praise or boast. The *Roemer* was a particularly democratic glass, not restricted to the humble society which its color and rather simple form might imply. Tables are seen in paintings of the period in which handsome *Roemers* are mounted in intricately wrought gilded stands. On the other hand, many peasant drinking scenes represent this vessel in much homelier surroundings.

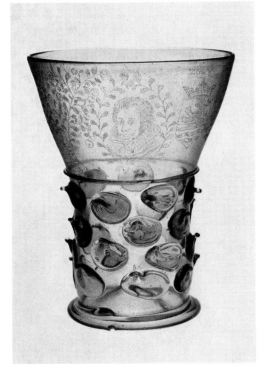

## (58) *Engraved Roemer*

NETHERLANDS           HT. $6\frac{5}{8}''$ (16.8 CM.)

1600-25             ACC. No. 56.3.24

Decoration not requiring glassmaking equipment was often carried out in special decorating shops or by amateurs. Diamond-point engraving, usually reserved for the finest *cristallo*, was sometimes applied to bottle-green glass. This green glass bears in diamond-point engraving the coats of arms of the seven provinces of the Netherlands and two portraits, probably the sons of William the Silent: the princes Maurits and Frederik.

## (59) *Engraved Beaker*

GERMANY          HT. 11¼″ (28.5 CM.)
BEFORE 1574          ACC. No. 50.3.1

Guilds and corporations of craftsmen and businessmen devoted to a single aspect of manufacture or trade played an important role in German daily life from the Middle Ages to the 19th century. At their meetings, large metal and glass containers served as communal drinking vessels. This beaker is inscribed with the names of members of a guild or brotherhood ranging over a period of 200 years. Dates and devices accompany the signatures scratched on the surface with a diamond stylus.

## (60) *Drinking Barrel*

NETHERLANDS          HT. 9¼″ (23.5 CM.)
17TH C.          ACC. No. 56.3.87

The immense size of many Northern drinking vessels suggests an almost superhuman capacity on the part of the user. A more temperate explanation is that the *Humpen* and barrel forms were communal vessels to be shared by several congenial drinkers. The thumb "cups" set in the hot, soft surface of the drinking barrel reproduced here assured the drinker of a firm grip—an important factor as forks had not yet come into popular use and the drinker's hands were apt to be greasy.

## (61)  *Trick Glass with a Stag*

GERMANY           TOTAL HT. 11″ (28.0 CM.)
EARLY 18TH C.           ACC. NO. 63.3.20

As early as the 18th Dynasty, Egyptian glassmakers
shaped their material in animal forms. Roman and
Islamic craftsmen continued the tradition, and the
glassblowers of Murano contributed incredible fan-
tasies to the menagerie built up over the centuries.
The stag in the glass depicted here is nothing more
than an elaborate straw, one of many "tricks"
designed to make drinking even more interesting.

## (62)  *Engraved Roemer*

SWEDEN, PROBABLY KUNGSHOLM GLASBRUK
                  HT. $14\frac{7}{16}$″ (37.0 CM.)
1ST QUARTER 18TH C.          ACC. No. 71.3.11

Sweden, lacking an independently developed glass
industry, was subject to foreign influence mainly
from Germany and England. German cut and engraved beakers and goblets were models for Swedish
craftsmen and they were successfully copied with
such minor modifications as the substitution by
order of specific coats of arms and other required
subject matter. This *Roemer*, decorated with an
inscription and flowers, clearly shows the popularity
of the German *Roemer* form.

53

(63) *Enameled Armorial Beaker*

GERMANY, PROBABLY SAXONY      HT. 8¾″ (22.2 CM.)

DATED 1671            ACC. NO. 51.3.215

ALARGE PROPORTION of the German glass of the 16th, 17th, and 18th centuries forms a group united by the common use of enamel and cold-painted decoration. The former technique consists of firing into the surface of a glass vessel a fusible paint composed of finely ground glass and/or metallic oxides; the latter is not fused but held on the surface with an adhesive such as oil or varnish and consequently is far more fragile than the product of fusion.

To cover a glass surface with enamel, either opaque or transparent, is a mode of decoration which was known to the Romans. The mosque lamps from Cairo and Damascus, made in the 13th and 14th centuries, represent a very high degree of technical ability in that medium. Venice revived this technique in the second half of the 15th century, applying color and gilt in jewel-like patterns. During the first half of the 16th century this medium was used to apply German coats of arms to glasses made in Venice but designed for sale in the North. Later in that century German craftsmen began enameling their own glasses primarily with armorial themes, and soon enameling on clear and, less frequently, on colored glass dominated the production of the late 16th and 17th centuries. Only between about 1650 and 1750 did engraving challenge the decorative supremacy enjoyed by enameling. The emphasis on this exacting technique is in odd contrast to the generally crude glass it embellishes.

## (64)  *Beaker or Spechter*

GERMANY, PROBABLY
SPESSART                    HT. 6½″ (16.5 CM.)
16TH C.                     ACC. No. 56.3.93

As early as in the 16th century glasshouses and decorators' shops in certain parts of Germany produced articles with characteristic features not generally found in other districts. Thus, the enamelers of Bohemia created in the late 16th century the giant *Reichsadler* and *Kurfursten Humpen* while the Fichtelgebirge produced beakers showing the highest elevation of this mountain chain. The *Spechter* illustrated here derives its name from the Spessart in central Germany. The cobblestone pattern was achieved by winding a heavy thread regularly around the vessel before it was inflated in a vertically ribbed mold. After final shaping and annealing, the vessel was gilded and enameled.

## (65)  *Beaker*

GERMANY, DRESDEN        HT. 8⅛″ (20.6 CM.)
DATED 1662              ACC. No. 56.3.90

In Germany, glass decorative techniques developed in Venice were applied to forms based on Northern traditions. The character of the ornamental devices often changed extensively to fit the more sturdy, clumsy shapes. The fine use of white filigree bands and the superior quality of the enamel, both characteristic of Saxon work, make this beaker worthy of the royal family whose coat of arms it bears.

56

## (66) *Reichsadler Humpen*
(Gift of Edwin J. Beinecke)

BOHEMIA    HT. 10 7/16″ (26.4 CM)

DATED 1574    ACC. No. 60.3.4

German enameling, so frequently applied to
the tall cylindrical *Humpen*, was largely a
popular art. Enameled vessels were produced
in large quantities in Bohemia and Germany
from the last quarter of the 16th through the
mid-18th century. The double-headed eagle
of the Holy Roman Empire bears on his breast
a crucifix indicating the God-willed protector-
ate of the Emperor, and on his wings the
shields of the Electors, nobles, and professions
owing allegiance to him.

## (67) *Enameled Tazza*

SPAIN, BARCELONA    D. 8 7/8″ (22.6 CM.)

CA. 1560-1600    ACC. No. 68.3.1

Venetian enameled glass also influenced Spanish glassmakers, but to a lesser extent than German
ones. This influence may be especially noted on a limited number of existing enameled glasses
produced in the Barcelona area. Like their German counterparts, the enameling on these glasses
is bold and simple, but the strong yellow and light green colors which predominate in the designs
composed of birds, dogs, and
foliate forms give them a dis-
tinction not found elsewhere
on enameled glass.

57

## (68) *Sepia-Enameled Humpen*

NETHERLANDS            HT. 10½″ (26.7 CM.)
EARLY 17TH C.            ACC. NO. 52.3.1

In the course of glass history there are many objects which are historically significant and describe events ranging from erotic adventures to Napoleonic campaigns; from Roman times to the present, glass vessels have supported a wide variety of commemorations including gladiatorial combats, the Mongol invasion, an infinite number of marriages, and the visit of the British royal couple to Canada. The scene on this enameled *Humpen* accompanied by a Latin text satirically commemorates the Spanish occupation of the Netherlands.

## (69) *Landscape, Reverse Painting on Glass, by Zeuner*

NETHERLANDS       17″ x 10 3/16″ (43.2 x 25.9 CM.)
LATE 18TH C.            ACC. NO. 53.3.32

The craftsmen of the 18th century outdid themselves in their eagerness to expand the decorative possibilities of their numerous techniques. A few of these were based on the plastic quality of glass, but many took advantage of the material as a support, both for its smoothness and for the deepening effect it has on the colors seen through it. The picture reproduced here, similar in subject to the work of 17th century Dutch Masters, such as Jan van Goyen, is composed of carefully engraved gold and silver leaf with a painted sky.

(70) *Beaker with Portraits of Emperor Leopold I
and Empress Margaret by Johann Schaper*

GERMANY, NUREMBERG      HT. 3 9/16″ (9.0 CM.)
3RD QUARTER 17TH C.      ACC. No. 51.3.122

The technique of staining and painting glass with a
brown or black grisaille was not confined to windows
but was also applied to glass vessels. Johann Schaper of
Nuremberg, who decorated both glass and pottery, employed a black, almost transparent enamel, *Schwarzlotmalerei*, similar to that used on contemporary stained
glass. In spite of the august personages portrayed on
this beaker, a very realistic fly has been enameled on the
bottom, visible when the drinker has drained the glass.

(71) *Enameled Bottle*

SILESIA      HT. 4 3/16″ (10.6 CM.)
CA. 1730      ACC. No. 62.3.69

During the latter years of the 17th and
in the early 18th century the so-called
*Schwarzlotmalerei* became increasingly
popular. In Silesia, Daniel Preissler
and his son Ignaz contributed to the
technique originated by Schaper. The
bottle reproduced here, in the style of
the Preisslers, represents a popular
hunting theme rendered in opaque
lines with sepia shadings. It may originally have had a silver, or silver-gilt
stopper.

59

## (72) *Opaque White Sprinkler*

VENICE           HT. 10⅞" (27.5 CM.)
2ND QUARTER 18TH C.      ACC. No. 51.3.315

The manufacture of *lattimo* or milk glass has
been described in Venetian manuscripts of
the 15th century. However, it was not produced in significant quantities before the
18th century. The decoration of this sprinkler
is characteristic of the enameled pieces made
by the Venetian glassmaking family Miotti;
its form suggests that it was made for the
Persian market.

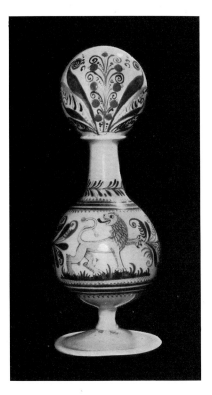

## (73) *Vase with Stopper*

FRANCE           HT. 9" (22.8 CM.)
EARLY 18TH C.        ACC. No. 56.3.26

The manufacture of porcelain exerted a particular
fascination on the glassmakers of France, Spain, and
Germany. Many of them were of Italian descent and,
no doubt, were familiar with the Venetian *lattimo*
glass—yet they enlarged on the Venetian repertoire,
introducing new designs which were further enriched
by enameled decoration of coats of arms, flowers,
and, occasionally, landscapes and dated inscriptions.
This type of vase with its ball stopper apparently
was made only in France.

60

(74)  *Teapot with an Enameled*
*Floral Design*

(Gift of Arthur A. Houghton, Jr.)

WESTERN EUROPE          HT. 5¼″ (13.4 CM.)
MID 18TH C.               ACC. No. 53.3.9

Milk-white opaque or translucent glass was
made in many of the glass producing centers
of Western Europe in direct competition with
porcelain. Like the 18th century teapot
reproduced here, opaque glass was enameled
in the same style as contemporary porcelain
and, in many cases, by the same artists.
Motifs employed generally ranged from imitative Chinese designs to native birds and
flowers painted in a naturalistic manner.

(75)  *Pepper Pot*

ENGLAND, PROBABLY BRISTOL    HT. 4 5/16″ (11.0 CM.)
CA. 3RD QUARTER 18TH C.        ACC. No. 50.2.52

Opaque white glass became popular during the period in which Chinese imports were particularly ad-
mired. Advertised as "mock china," it was capably
enameled in several glassmaking centers of which
Bristol is the best known. This pepper pot is decorated in the popular rococo style, and the influence
of China is evident both in the choice of subject and
the treatment.

(76) *Engraved Goblet*

GERMANY, NUREMBERG      HT. WITH COVER $14\frac{11}{16}''$
(37.3 CM.)

CA. 1660-80      ACC. NO. 56.3.79

Two great traditions dominate the history of glass in Europe from the 15th century onwards. The Southern tradition, with Venice and Murano as center, created refined masterworks of great fragility and intricacy, casting its influence as far away as Sweden and England. The Northern tradition, on the other hand, repeated a few basic types in rather crude glass until it slowly became receptive to the Southern impact. Venetian glass was either faithfully copied or single motifs and decorative techniques adapted and absorbed into an indigenous style. The manufacturers of more luxurious glasses and the decorators working with them were often associated with towns famous for their cultural standing or their political importance. Such centers were fertile ground for new developments in the arts, and princely families vied with each other for the patronage of especially promising craftsmen.

It is understandable, therefore, that in a metropolis like Prague, where Emperor Rudolph II had amassed one of the greatest art collections in the world, the techniques used to carve rock crystal should be applied to glass. In 1609 Caspar Lehman was granted an exclusive privilege to engrave glass. His discovery, new to his contemporaries but actually almost as old as glassmaking, set the scene for the future history of German glass decoration. It began to replace enameling by the end of the 17th century and was a most suitable decorative medium for both German potash and English lead glasses, two new glass materials coming into great popularity at this time. Lehman's heritage was taken over by a few Nuremberg engravers whose works compare favorably with the best engraved glasses of all times. This covered *Pokal* bears a scene in intaglio similar to glasses attributed to Hermann Schwinger.

## (77) *Engraved Goblet with a Hunting Scene*

GERMANY, NUREMBERG      HT. 11¼″ (28.5 CM.)
CA. 1660-70      ACC. No. 50.3.25

The heavy, German potash-chalk glass, developed toward the end of the 17th century, made possible the perfection of the engraving techniques introduced to the glass decorator's repertoire almost a century before. A design was drawn onto the plain surface of the glass. Then the vessel was pressed against a rapidly rotating wheel of stone or copper which either cut into the glass directly or with the help of abrasives. Wheels of different sizes determined the width of the cut and, the higher the desired effect of relief, the deeper the cut. The abraded surface was either left rough or polished down to heighten the brilliance of the "crystal."

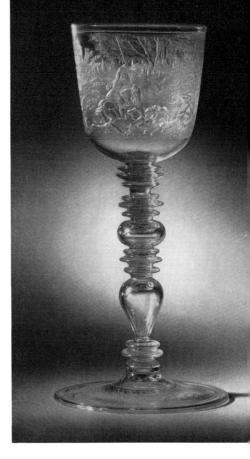

## (78) *Covered Beaker*

Attributed to Gottfried Spiller
GERMANY, POTSDAM      HT. 10″ (25.4 CM.)
CA. 1700-10      ACC. No. 61.3.8

At the end of the 17th century, engraving styles were becoming more sculptural, and artists, such as Spiller, were combining intaglio and relief techniques to achieve more dramatic effects. Though a clear, brilliant glass was predominantly used, much experimentation was conducted to produce a red glass. This beaker in a deep, virtually flawless ruby marks the culmination of these attempts.

64

**(79)  Covered Goblet**

POSSIBLY ENGRAVED BY FRIEDRICH WINTER

SILESIA                                 HT. 13½″ (34.3 CM.)

CA. 1700                                 ACC. No. 61.3.9

During the early 18th century, the portraiture of princely
rulers, combined with their coats of arms and other in-
signia of their office, were among the most often depicted
subjects. Goblets and other glasses with these motifs
were suitable for official gifts and, as a result, many were
preserved in the treasuries of European rulers and have
survived the passage of time.

**(80)  Engraved Goblet**

PROBABLY ENGRAVED BY HEINRICH JAGER

GERMANY                                 HT. 14¾″ (37.5 CM.)

CA. 1700-10                              ACC. No. 72.3.16

The range of subject matter employed by 18th century
glass decorators was extremely broad. To the traditional
themes of coats of arms, symbolic personifications of the
Empire, the ages of man, and the four seasons, they added
subjects drawn from courtly life, trade, and, less frequently, mythology. In this example the bowl is engraved
with the Three Graces and *megaira*, or Jealousy; the
cover with buildings in a pastoral setting.

## (81) *Engraved Goblet*

PROBABLY ENGRAVED BY GEORG F. KILLINGER

GERMANY, NUREMBERG                 HT. 8 1/16″ (20.5 CM.)

CA. 1725                                       ACC. NO. 64.3.7

In the early 18th century, Nuremberg continued to be one
of several engraving centers in Germany. Georg Friedrich
Killinger was one of the foremost engravers working there
at this time. His work included delicately executed landscapes with superbly rendered architectural details, pastoral scenes, coats of arms, and inscriptions. These were
almost always surrounded by wreaths and, frequently, an
array of decorative motifs typical of the period. The
reverse of this goblet bears the inscription "Non Vilescit
Piscis et Hospes."

## (82) *Diamond-Point Engraved Goblet*

PROBABLY ENGRAVED BY WILLEM MOOLEYSER

NETHERLANDS                          HT. 7 15/16″ (19.8 CM.)

1685-97                                     ACC. NO. 58.3.175

Copper-wheel engraving on glass, in spite of its popularity,
did not replace the age-old technique of diamond-point
engraving. After the first Venetian diamond-engraved
tazzas and bowls reached Northern lands in the 16th
century, the Dutch in particular took a liking to this technique. The brittle, Venetian-type *cristallo* lent itself particularly well to scratch engraving, taking the impress of a
sharp point with precision, yet allowing the engraver considerable freedom of movement. Most goblets engraved in
this manner in the Netherlands were decorated by amateurs as a hobby. Many of these glasses bear mottoes and
devices in a flourishing baroque style or simple scenes of
friendship, as on this goblet.

## (83) *Goblet attributed to Giacomo Verzelini*

PROBABLY ENGRAVED BY ANTHONY DE LYSLE
ENGLAND, LONDON, PROBABLY BROAD STREET GLASSHOUSE
DATED 1577     ACC. NO. 50.2.1     HT. 8″ (20.3 CM.)

In 1575 England took a great step toward the founding of a national glass industry which was to emerge as a distinct and vital achievement in the 18th century. This occurred when Giacomo Verzelini of Venice was granted the right to make Venetian-type glass for twenty-one years by Queen Elizabeth I upon condition that he teach Englishmen his art. This goblet attributed to Verzelini and decorated in the traditional Venetian technique of diamond-point engraving is the earliest known dated English glass drinking vessel.

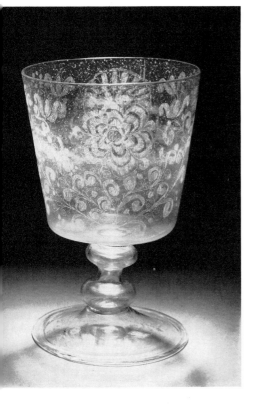

## (84) *Engraved Goblet*

ENGLAND                    HT. 9⅝″ (24.5 CM.)
CA. 2ND-3RD QUARTER 17TH C.    ACC. NO. 55.2.1

A group of businessmen with considerable foresight acquired Verzelini's privilege in 1592 and thus began a succession of monopolies which lasted for nearly 70 years. Most famous of the monopolists, Sir Robert Mansell, operated glasshouses in London as well as other parts of the country. He is better known for his astute business sense than for the quality of the glass his companies produced. This pre-Restoration, diamond-point engraved soda glass goblet with its large bucket bowl set on a dumbbell knop may possibly be an example from the Mansell period although this attribution is yet unproven.

(85)  *Pair of Enameled Armorial Goblets*
*Signed "Beilby invt. et pinxt."*

ENGLAND                    HT. 8¾″ (22.3 CM.)

CA. 1760-70                ACC. No. 50.2.8

ENGLAND'S CONTRIBUTION to the history of glass is of singular importance and stems from the development of lead glass by George Ravenscroft in 1676. This material permitted unprecedented scientific and artistic advances, being softer, clearer, and more brilliant than soda glass. These basic characteristics resulted in the development of a distinct English style which otherwise might have remained true to the Venetian traditions, originally so highly treasured. Subsequently influenced by German-born George I, King of England after the death of Queen Anne, and channeled by the dictates of national taste, the English drinking vessel developed into a capacious glass of sturdy and striking proportion, emphasizing the beauty of the metal by simple, unadorned forms.

The popularity of these new glasses both in England and abroad encouraged rapid expansion within the glass industry. The government took advantage of these developments by leveling a tax based on the weight of the raw materials required. This burden increased gradually, forcing many houses to close, move to Ireland, or find ways to justify the high prices necessitated by the tax. Various decorative techniques were employed to heighten the value of table glass, and although the market was limited, those glassmakers who survived produced some of England's finest glass. These goblets, decorated by England's foremost enamelers, the Beilbys, about 1760, bear the arms of the Earls of Pembroke and Montgomery and are executed in the flowery *rococo* style of the period.

69

(86)  *The Buggin Bowl*

ENGLAND, LONDON, SAVOY GLASSHOUSE OF
GEORGE RAVENSCROFT   D. 4¹³⁄₁₆″ (12.2 CM.)
CA. 1675                          ACC. NO. 63.2.7

The Restoration in 1660 introduced a
period of scientific research and witnessed
the final development of clear lead "crystal" by George Ravenscroft in 1676. Dr.
Christopher Merret's translation of Neri's
*L'Arte Vetraria* into English revealed
previously unknown technical secrets.
Together with the financial backing of
the Glass Sellers' Company, manufacturers and promotors of glassmaking,
Ravenscroft was able to develop a glass
that could be made from English raw
materials. This bowl bears the diamond-
point engraved coat of arms of Butler
Buggin.

(87)  *Goblet with Raven's Head Seal*

ENGLAND, LONDON, SAVOY GLASSHOUSE OF
GEORGE RAVENSCROFT          HT. CA. 7³⁄₈″ (18.8 CM.)
CA. 1676-78                        ACC. NO. 50.2.2

Much of the early lead glass made in the Savoy Glasshouse is crizzled, the outer surface of the glass having
decomposed due to an excessive amount of alkali in the
formula from which the glass was melted. When this
technical problem had been solved many lead glasses
were marked with a glass seal as proof that they were
made from the improved formula. On this goblet one
of the raspberry prunts has been replaced by the
famous seal, bearing a raven's head, the trademark of
George Ravenscroft.

70

## (88) *Anglo-Venetian Goblet*

ENGLAND            HT. $10\frac{9}{16}''$ (26.8 CM.)
CA. 1685            ACC. NO. 50.2.27

English glassmakers continued to make drinking vessels in the preferred Venetian manner after lead glass was generally adopted for the making of fine tableware. The characteristics of the new metal were not, however, adaptable to Venetian designs. To show its particular qualities properly, lead glass required heavier, simpler forms than the very flexible soda glass *cristallo* of Murano. This goblet, made of lead glass, is decorated in the Venetian manner and represents a transitional phase in the evolution of a distinctly English style.

## (89) *Jacobite Goblet*

ENGLAND            HT. 8″ (20.3 CM.)
CA. 1740-50            ACC. NO. 50.2.110

Paramount in importance among the many motifs engraved on 18th century English glasses were those dedicated to the Jacobite cause which favored the return of the Stuarts to the throne of England, then occupied by the Hanoverian Georges. Generally engraved by special order of some secret society, most of the glasses are embellished with disguised symbols such as a rose, a thistle, and a stricken oak, perhaps representing the Crown of England, Scotland, and the House of Stuart. This goblet, more crudely engraved than its German counterparts, bears the portrait of the Old Pretender, James III.

## (90) *Diamond-Stipple Engraved Goblet Signed "F. Greenwood"*

ENGLAND AND NETHERLANDS    HT. 9⅞″ (25.0 CM.)

DATED 1746    ACC. No. 50.2.10

Undecorated English vessels of lead glass traveled frequently to the Continent during the 18th century where they were decorated by Dutch and German engravers. Franz Greenwood (1680-1761) developed the technique of stipple engraving introduced by Anna Roemers Visscher in 1646. The portraits and still lifes executed in this medium are often based on prints of the period. Although the technique was further improved by David Wolff, the free robust style of the Greenwood pieces has yet to be surpassed.

## (91) *Diamond-Stipple Engraved Goblet*

PROBABLY BY DAVID WOLFF

ENGLAND AND NETHERLANDS    HT. 7¾″ (19.7 CM.)

CA. 1775-85    ACC. No. 53.3.28

A diamond point when repeatedly tapped against the surface of a glass produces a pattern of minute dots which, by refracting light, appear white in contrast to the untouched surface around them. When applied by such a master as David Wolff, the dots form an image of great delicacy. The English Newcastle-type glass reproduced here has been embellished with a romantic Fragonard-like scene typical of Wolff's fine work.

## (92) *Engraved Bowl*

ENGLAND          Ht. 5½″ (14.0 cm.)
Ca. 1760          Acc. No. 64.2.11

Though the relatively soft English lead glass lent itself well to engraving, that craft never reached in England the perfection attained on the Continent, nor does it appear to have been practiced with any consistency. This bowl is unusual in that a highly sophisticated design, including the mottoes of the Walpole and Fitzwilliam families, has been engraved on a green, non-lead glass.

## (93) *Cut Sweetmeat*

IRELAND          Ht. 4 9/16″ (11.6 cm.)
LAST QUARTER 18TH C.  Acc. No. 50.2.43

Irish glass is basically the result of the glasscutter's art. The fluidity of the material, a property apparent in so many forms throughout ths history of glass, as well as the "gaffer's" tooling, are obscured by the cutter's wheel which itself seems to create the shape and surface pattern of the vessel. This approach, exemplified by the Waterford-type glass of the late 18th and early 19th centuries, was immediately popular, and its influence is still felt in cutting shops throughout the world.

### (94) *Candleholder*

IRELAND       Hᴛ. 9¾″ (25.0 ᴄᴍ.)

Cᴀ. 1785       Aᴄᴄ. No. 50.2.21

Although the origin of glass chandeliers, candelabra, and candleholders can be traced back to 17th-century Venice, it was in England and Ireland during the late 18th century that these forms reached their fullest development. The heavy cutting which developed during the second half of the century brought out the full brilliance of the lead glass, and its high refractive powers multiplied the illumination obtained from wax candles.

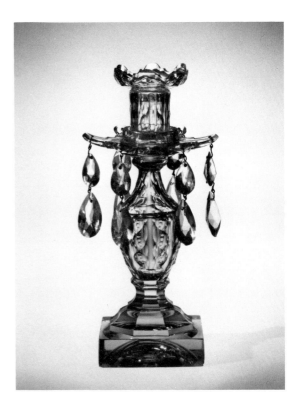

### (95) *Farm House*

NᴇᴛHᴇʀLᴀɴᴅs ᴏʀ Eɴɢʟᴀɴᴅ

      L. 16⅛″ (41.0 ᴄᴍ.)

Dᴀᴛᴇᴅ 1803       Aᴄᴄ. No. 63.3.80

Itinerant lampworkers who required little equipment to perform their trade traveled extensively in the 17th and 18th centuries, performing in country fairs or setting up temporary shops. They specialized in executing minutely descriptive scenes, which by the mid-18th century tended to become more and more secular in nature. This farm house made entirely of glass marks the last flowering of this art which by the mid-19th century had become a mere sideshow curiosity.

74

## (96) *Tumbler with Portrait Medallion by J. J. Mildner*

AUSTRIA

DATED 1792

HT. 4½″ (11.4 CM.)

ACC. NO. 54.3.12

In the 18th century a variation of the old Roman technique of laminating a layer of gold between two pieces of glass was revived. It is called *Zwischengoldglas*. A variant of this technique involving the use of gold or silver leaf and red lacquer was skillfully developed by Johann Joseph Mildner, often in combination with miniature portraits on parchment. In addition to the medallion on the side, many Mildner tumblers contain similar laminated decorations in the base, but in this instance the base is plain.

## (97) *Enameled Tumbler with a View of Meissen by Samuel Mohn*

GERMANY

EARLY 19TH C.

HT. 4″ (10.2 CM.)

ACC. NO. 51.3.198

For centuries opaque enamels have been employed in the decoration of glass. They have been applied almost invariably in flat masses of bright color occasionally accented with linear brush work in black. Intaglio engravers, on the other hand, delighted in the rendering of form and in creating an illusion of depth, using the glass as a support for their pictorial interpretation. In the early 19th century, Samuel Mohn, employing translucent enamels, painted realistic scenes incredibly minute in detail. Views of cities, maps of celebrated battle fields, and genre scenes were colorfully executed on tumblers and decanters.

75

## (98) *Covered Beaker, Balloon Ascent*

RUSSIA, BAKHMETEV GLASSWORKS

HT. 5½″ (14.6 CM.)

CA. 1800-20                    ACC. No. 64.3.118

In style and form, Russian glass in the 18th and
19th centuries was greatly influenced by Bohemian and German glass production. This double-
walled beaker, containing a depiction of Lunardi's
balloon ascent, which occurred in 1791, is a variation and a development of Bohemian *Zwischengoldglas*. This detailed scene, made of paper, straw
and other materials, has been meticulously assembled between the two walls of glass, which are
sealed at the top. It is a rare representation of a
scene which stirred men's imaginations.

## (99) *Engraved Portrait Signed "D. Biman"*

BOHEMIA, PRAGUE                D. 3¾″ (9.5 CM.)

DATED 1834                     ACC. No. 65.3.68

Throughout the 19th century, Bohemian engravers continued to produce some of the most outstanding work
decorated in this manner. Unequivocally, between 1826-
1857, Dominik Biman was the foremost engraver of his
era. Much of his work was associated with various spas and
included numerous commissions from the wealthy who
visited them. The portrait illustrated is indicative not only
of his great mechanical skill, but it also illustrates his
ability to portray his subject with sensitivity and per-
ception.

### (100) *Covered Goblet*

BOHEMIA       HT. WITH COVER 17″ (43.2 CM.)
CA. MID-19TH C.       ACC. NO. 54.3.104

Bohemia, with her numerous glass factories and decorating shops, was first among European glass producing countries in the 19th century. Having a great variety of clear and colored glass at their disposal, cutters, engravers, and enamelers used it as a vehicle to demonstrate, often with great extravagance, their unequaled prowess. They worked either alone or in factories which sometimes employed over a hundred specialists to satisfy the demand for the fashionable Bohemian glass.

### (101) *Ewer*

SIGNED: W. FRITSCHE
ENGLAND, STROURBRIDGE       HT. $15\frac{3}{16}$″ (38.5 CM.)
DATED 1886       ACC. NO. 54.2.16

In the 19th century, as in the preceding centuries, carved rock crystal maintained its role as a source of inspiration to glassmakers and engravers alike. Rarely has the glass cutter more successfully captured the character of the stone than in this late Victorian ewer. William Fritsche, who emigrated from his native Bohemia to England and became master engraver for Thomas Webb, created an intricate and technically astonishing pattern in high relief and intaglio into the heavy clear glass. The practice of polishing the abraded surface left by the engraver's tools was known as "rock crystal engraving."

77

(102)  *Pair of Millefiori Vases*

FRANCE, CLICHY          HT. CA. 9⅝″ (24.5 CM.)

CA. 1845-50             ACC. NO. 53.3.60

THOUGH glassmaking has a long and distinguished tradition in France, its style is generally eclectic in character, borrowing forms and decoration from Venetian, German, and English traditions. Louis XIV's minister Colbert banned the importation of Venetian mirrors and encouraged local manufacture with the result that new casting techniques were evolved, and French mirrors became famous throughout Europe. In other types of glass, French glassmakers lagged far behind; toward the end of the 18th century several glasshouses were established for the purpose of competing with English and German imports. By the middle of the 19th century French *cristal* was ranked among the finest. Among the contributions of this epoch the revival of millefiori decoration and its application to new forms is of great interest. These two large vases, each bearing the name *Clichy* in a tiny cane, are among the rarest types of millefiori glass. Paperweights were the most frequently produced objects in this exacting technique. The large Salamander weight is a variant in that, instead of having a multitude of small canes imbedded in the clear matrix, there is one glass salamander, exquisitely modeled to form the whole composition.

(103) *Paperweight*
(From the Amory Houghton Gift)
FRANCE, POSSIBLY ST. LOUIS
D. 4¾″ (12.1 CM.)
AFTER 1848          ACC. NO. 55.3.79

79

(104) *Giant Carved Bottle*

(Gift of Benjamin D. Bernstein)

CHINA, PROBABLY CH'IEN LUNG        HT. 19¼″ (48.9 CM.)

PROBABLY 18TH C.               ACC. NO. 57.6.10

STRATIFIED EYE BEADS excavated in China and attributed to the late Chou Dynasty (1122-255 B.C.) were influenced by Egyptian eye beads with which they have many characteristics in common. A number of ceremonial *Pi* discs which symbolized heaven, also of the early period, are known in glass although far less frequently than in jade. It has been suggested that many obviously oriental glass objects were made from glass fused in the West and reheated and worked by Eastern craftsmen.

In spite of the high degree of craftsmanship evident in Chinese glass, this medium seems to have been of interest only for its potential as an imitator of more precious materials. The inherent qualities of glass, plasticity and transparency, were generally ignored and emphasis placed on attempts to duplicate the textures of jade, quartz, and other natural stones.

The most prolific period in Chinese glassmaking occurred during the reign of the Emperor Ch'ien Lung (1735-1795). This large bottle has an overlay of red glass carved with a very elaborate scene depicting equestrian warriors, buildings, and nobles, all set in a fantastic stagelike setting.

The sculpture of clear glass on the right, representing a Buddha, appears to have been based on a famous north Siamese rock crystal image. As no glass industry is known to have existed in Siam or Burma, it has been assumed that this and similar objects were either imported from Europe through England's East India Company or, more likely, commissioned in China. Its grey-bluish tint and relative purity place it among the more successful imitations of natural stones.

(105) *Buddha*

POSSIBLY CHINA
HT. 5¾″ (14.6 CM.)
3RD QUARTER OF THE 19TH C.
ACC. NO. 56.6.10

(106) *Pair of Enameled Ch'ien Lung Vases*
(Gift of Arthur A. Houghton, Jr.)

CHINA                    Hт. 6½″ (16.5 см.)

18ᴛʜ c.                   Acc. No. 53.6.1

U NDER the protection and encouragement of Emperor Ch'ien Lung, the porcelain and glass manufactories developed and prospered; much of the production consisted of intricately cut belt buckles, snuff bottles, and objects of personal adornment. Overlaid in contrasting colors and decorated with the engraver's wheel, the bowls and bottles made during this time have an almost boisterous splendor completely unlike the cameo overlays of the Roman Empire. Stone carving, however, was not the only source of inspiration for these accomplished artisans. The close contact with the Imperial porcelain manufactory caused craftsmen also to make glass vessels in opaque white material. This type is not without antecedents: the Daphne Ewer (figure 14), made in Syria 1500 years before, represents a majestic counterpart, though not prototype, of Chinese milk glass.

The striking similarity between the world-famous "china" and its imitations in glass is proof of the technical knowledge of the oriental glassmakers. The delicate enameled decoration on these two glass vases is probably the work of artists attached to the Imperial porcelain manufactory.

(107)  *Sugar Bowl*

UNITED STATES, POSSIBLY WISTARBERG OR GLASSBORO
PROBABLY LAST QUARTER 18TH C.

HT. 6⅛″ (15.5 CM.)
ACC. NO. 50.4.2

THE HISTORY of glassmaking in America before 1900 is unique among glass histories in that it records in terms of known glassmakers the birth and growth of a national glass industry. Continuing and occasionally combining different European traditions, Americans invented the first machine for pressing glass. This invention—the most important since the discovery of the blowpipe—was the first in a series of technical achievements which have since completely altered the nature of the glass industry and, in many cases, of glass itself.

In 1608 the London Company, anxious to increase England's sources of supply, constructed a glasshouse at Jamestown in the colony of Virginia, thereby establishing America's first industry. Although glass was actually melted there, little remains of production: the hardships of the New World forced its glassmakers to abandon their craft in favor of agriculture. The second attempt, made in 1621, was equally unsuccessful, and the founding of the present industry must be credited to Caspar Wistar who was the first American to successfully operate a glass manufactory over a long period of time. Established in Salem County, New Jersey, in 1739, the so-called Wistarberg Works produced the usual bottles and window panes as economic staples. In addition, a number of handsome individual pieces, free-blown and probably intended for family and friends, have been attributed to this factory. Usually made from ordinary amber, olive, and green glass, and generally following Continental glassmaking traditions, objects of this type were produced in many glasshouses through the end of the 18th and well into the 19th century. These distinct objects are known by the generic term "South Jersey type."

### (108) *Pair of Candlesticks*

UNITED STATES, PROBABLY WISTARBERG GLASSWORKS
CA. 1740-77                    HT. 7¾″ (19.6 CM.)
                                    ACC. No. 50.4.1

The South Jersey tradition in American glassmaking is characterized by individual expression rather than industrial organization. The glassblowers who arrived from Europe were not master craftsmen leaving the service of kings and princes but rather were practical glassmen, makers of bottles and window panes. The objects they made for their own purposes are generally simple and closely related to the pewter and furniture of the period, occasionally naively ornate with chicken-shape finials and pincered glass handles.

### (109) *Blue Sugar Bowl*

UNITED STATES, POSSIBLY MANHEIM, PENNSYLVANIA
GLASSWORKS OF HENRY W. STIEGEL
                                    HT. 6⅛″ (15.5 CM.)
CA. 1765-74                    ACC. No. 50.4.18

A second glassmaking tradition is attributed to Henry William Stiegel, the self-titled baron of Manheim, Pennsylvania. In contrast to the South Jersey type of glass, the Stiegel-type is generally made from clear or artificially colored glass. Tableware was part of the factory's output, usually decorated by enameling, engraving, or pattern-molding. In serving a society dominated by English taste, Stiegel-type glass includes many elegant objects made in the English style in addition to the numerous German peasant types of glassware.

## (110) *Amethyst Flask*

UNITED STATES, POSSIBLY MANHEIM, PENNSYLVANIA
GLASSWORKS OF HENRY W. STIEGEL

HT. CA. 5⅛″ (13.0 CM.)

CA. 1765-74                          ACC. NO. 50.4.22

To the Stiegel factories in their eleven years of
existence (1763-1774) have been attributed almost
every type of European peasant glass which found
its way to America. Many pieces which circum-
stantial evidence identifies with Stiegel are indistinguishable from their Continental counterparts. A
few objects, however, have certain characteristics
which are believed to have originated in America.
The diamond-daisy pattern on this pocket flask is
a specific example.

## (111) *The Tobias and The Angel Covered Tumbler*

UNITED STATES, NEW BREMEN GLASS
MANUFACTORY OF JOHN FREDERICK AMELUNG

HT. 11⅞″ (30.1 CM.)

DATED 1788                          ACC. NO. 55.4.37

John Frederick Amelung came to the state of
Maryland from Germany in 1784. His belief that a
well managed glasshouse would be personally prof-
itable and nationally appreciated proved to be in-
correct, and the Amelung works in New Bremen
was sold in 1795. His interest in achieving a colorless glass and in copper-wheel engraving was
responsible for some of the most handsome and historically important glass made in America before
1800.

(112)  *Lily-Pad Pitcher*

UNITED STATES, POSSIBLY LANCASTER OR LOCKPORT GLASSWORKS

CA. 1840-60         HT. $7\frac{1}{16}$″ (18. CM.) ACC. NO. 50.4.450

After the War of Independence, glassmaking in the United States continued to suffer from lack of support, both public and private. The state governments were slow to offer encouragement to companies in the form of loans and exemptions from taxes. The federal government further failed to realize the need for adequate protection in the form of tariff regulations. Glasshouses closed and the men migrated, some to the Midwest where the economic importance of liquor insured bottle manufacturers of a market and where transportation difficulties promised less competition. The growing national fervor which culminated in the War of 1812 brought a short era of prosperity and encouraged the establishment of many new glasshouses. With the signing of the Treaty of Ghent, a flood of English glass poured into American ports, and by 1820 more than half of the extant glass companies had failed. The final establishment of the glass industry on a sound financial basis was accomplished by the protective tariff enacted in 1824 and by the development of mechanical means of production.

During this entire period and well into the second half of the 19th century, handsome utilitarian vessels continued to be made in the South Jersey tradition. A decorative device of particular interest is illustrated by the pitcher reproduced here. Known as a lily-pad, and apparently having no direct European prototype, it consists of a superimposed gather of glass which has been tooled into a series of projections and drawn up the sides of the object.

## (113) *The Hornet and Peacock Decanter*

UNITED STATES, PITTSBURGH, PA., BIRMINGHAM
GLASS WORKS OF CHARLES IHMSEN     HT. 11″ (27.9 CM.)
CA. 1813                        Acc. No. 55.4.44

The decline of the glass industry in the East which followed the failures of the Stiegel and Amelung factories
forced many glassmakers to search for better opportuni-
ties in the west. A large number settled in the Pittsburgh
area which soon became a flourishing glass center. Charles
Ihmsen had come from Germany in 1795 and started a
factory in Baltimore in association with Amelung's son.
In 1810 he moved to Pittsburgh where he engraved this
decanter depicting the naval victory of the American
privateer Hornet over the H.M.S. Peacock. In later
years the Pittsburgh area produced some of the finest
"crystal" made in this country.

## (114) *Cut Glass Decanter*

UNITED STATES, PITTSBURGH, PITTSBURGH FLINT GLASS
WORKS OF BAKEWELL, PAGE AND BAKEWELL
                       HT. 10¾″ (27.3 CM.)
CA. 1825                        Acc. No. 67.4.8

Bakewell and Company, founded in 1807, produced all
types of glass from flasks, bottles, and window glass to
fine cut and engraved tablewares until it closed in 1882.
However, it is best known for its fine cut glass, such as the
decanter illustrated, bearing a typical Anglo-Irish
pattern of the period. This is not surprising, since many
of Bakewell's employees were English, and accounts of
visitors to the factory refer to ". . . fine glass cut to the
latest London patterns."

90

### (115)  *Blown-Three-Mold Decanter*

UNITED STATES, POSSIBLY SANDWICH, MASS.,
BOSTON AND SANDWICH GLASS WORKS  HT. 9¾″ (25.0 CM.)
CA. 1825-35                              ACC. NO. 50.4.142

The search for new methods permitting mass production
eventually led to the evolution of forms which are re-
garded today as typically American. The old technique of
blowing glass in a mold made of several parts was improved with the use of iron molds which, in addition to
their durability, could be carved in the most elaborate
designs, often based on cut glass patterns. The decoration
often reflects the 19th century's interest in past architectural or decorative designs such as the gothic arch. The
presence of the word *gin* emphasizes the imitative nature
of this type of object, for expensive cut decanters generally had silver tabs, engraved with the name of the beverage, hung around their necks.

### (116)  *Pictorial Flask with the American Eagle—Columbia*

UNITED STATES       HT. 6⅝″ (16.8 CM.)
CA. 1825-40         ACC. NO. 50.4.324

The strong national pride which accompanied so much activity in America
between 1815 and 1870 is well exemplified by a series of mold-blown flasks and
calabash bottles. Known collectively as
American pictorial flasks, these were
decorated by being expanded in incised
hinged molds bearing a wide variety of
images including Masonic symbols, national heroes, presidential candidates,
visiting dignitaries, and such patriotic
emblems as the flag and eagle.

## (117)  *Lacy Pressed Creamer*

UNITED STATES, PITTSBURGH, FORT PITT
GLASS WORKS OF R. B. CURLING
& SONS                    HT. 4″ (10.2 CM.)
CA. 1830                  ACC. NO. 50.4.205

The development of mechanical pressing revolutionized the glass industry and
even changed the physical appearance
of glass. The dull foggy effect caused by
contact with the mold under pressure
was enlivened by decorating every inch
of the surface—originally with patterns
based on cut glass designs and later with
new combinations of motifs frequently
incorporating elements from the classic
revival. The first twenty-five years of
pressed glass manufacture between 1825
and 1850 are known as the Lacy Period
because of this emphasis on over-all
detailed decoration.

## (118)  *Pressed Pattern Glass Celery Vase*

UNITED STATES, PROBABLY SANDWICH, MASS.
BOSTON AND SANDWICH GLASS WORKS          HT. 8$\frac{7}{16}$″ (21.5 CM.)
CA. 1855-70                              ACC. NO. 68.4.12

The molds to produce the intricate lacy pressed glass were
expensive. About 1840, partly because of the depression caused
by the closing of the national banks by Andrew Jackson in 1837,
and partly because of developing technology and changing
taste, designs for pressed glass were greatly simplified, ushering
in a style known as pressed pattern glass. The first of these very
simple patterns, such as *Ashburton* and *Argus*, was followed by
somewhat more elaborate designs like the *Comet* pattern celery
vase illustrated. These popular patterns were frequently made
in full services, often by more than one manufacturer. Some
remained popular for several decades. In the last third of the
19th century, both the designs and the quality of the glass
tended to degenerate.

92

## (119)  *Cut Plate*

UNITED STATES, CORNING, NEW YORK
T. G. HAWKES & CO.     D. 13¼″ (34.0 CM.)
CA. 1900                    ACC. NO. 51.4.536

During the last quarter of the 19th century, cut glass reached the peak of its popularity in the United States. Exploiting to the fullest the high index of refraction of a very brilliant lead glass, large numbers of firms vied with each other in creating complicated patterns. Cut glass remained in vogue until the first years of the 20th century but finally succumbed to cheap imitations, partly pressed, which flooded the European and American markets.

## (120)  *Peachblow Vase*

UNITED STATES, WHEELING, WEST VIRGINIA
HOBBS, BROCKUNIER AND CO.
                    HT. 9⅞″ (25.0 CM.)
1886-91            ACC. NO. 50.4.328

The Victorian love of color and elaborate decoration, combined with a developed chemical technology, resulted in the production of a wide variety of Art Glass during the last quarter of the 19th century in America and abroad. Shaded, or particolored glasses, such as Amberina, Peachblow, and Burmese, were especially popular, as were enameled and gilded glasses, often exotic in form and decoration. This Morgan vase simulated in form and color a Chinese ceramic vase in the collection of Mrs. Charles Morgan which caught the popular fancy when it was sold for what was considered a fabulous sum.

93

## (121) Encased and Acid-Etched Vase by Emile Gallé

FRANCE, NANCY      HT. 12⅝″ (32.5 CM.)
CA. 1885-1900      ACC. NO. 51.3.168

Emile Gallé ranks high on the list of artists who have used glass as a medium of artistic expression. Thoroughly imbued in the traditions of glassmaking and aware of the technological advances which were the product of the Industrial Revolution, he played a leading role in the evolution of Art Nouveau. Rejecting the sterile precision characteristic of the new mechanical techniques, he used floral motifs with great freedom and imagination.

## (122) Vase

SIGNED "LOUIS C. TIFFANY FURNACE FAVRILE"
UNITED STATES, TIFFANY FURNACES,
CORONA, LONG ISLAND      HT. 11¹³⁄₁₆″ (30.1 CM.)
1910-20      ACC. NO. 64.4.31

Louis Comfort Tiffany first became noted for his stained glass windows, ecclesiastical and secular, but in 1893 he turned his attention to the design and production of glass objects. He became the foremost proponent of the Art Nouveau style in America, and his iridescent "Favrile" glass exerted a strong influence on some European glassmakers, including Loetz of Austria.

94

## (123) *Mermaid*

FRANCE, FRANCOIS DECORCHEMONT

HT. 13½″ (33.0 CM.)

CA. 1925-35                    ACC. NO. 53.3.14

Some of the glass produced after the first World War
is evidence of a reaction against the precious exotic
character of the Art Nouveau glass of Gallé, Daum,
and Tiffany. Artists like Decorchemont and Maurice
Marinot were concerned with massive forming and
decorative techniques revealing the sculptural po-
tentiality of glass rather than the polished flowing
forms of their predecessors. The results were often
vigorous, rather heavy pictorial representations, but
the simple vessel forms and stone-like textures have
survived the changing tastes of the last few decades.

## (124) *Engraved Beaker Signed "MR" and with the Lobmeyr emblem*

DESIGNED BY MICHAEL POWOLNY

HT. 5¼″ (13.3 CM.)

ENGRAVED BY MAX RÖSSLER

AUSTRIA, VIENNA, J. & L. LOBMEYR

1917                          ACC. NO. 69.3.2

The J. & L. Lobmeyr firm, established in
1823, gained, over the years, a justifiable
reputation for fine engraved and other
decorated glass. The fine quality of its products and designs continued into the 20th
century, as illustrated by this beaker engraved with representations of Happiness,
Health, and Joy. This piece represents the
finest engraved glass of the period.

(125) *Covered Urn, "The Negro Hut"*
DESIGNED BY SIMON GATE
SWEDEN, ORREFORS      HT. $10\frac{5}{16}''$ (26.2 CM.)
1927      ACC. NO. 68.3.16

In 1916 and 1917, Orrefors Glassworks, in an unprecedented move, hired two artists to design its glass:
Simon Gate and Edvard Hald. This bold move soon
placed Orrefors in a position of leadership in the glass
industry and influenced glass design in Europe for
many years to come. The simple, direct representation
of this subject, entitled "The Negro Hut," illustrates
both an effective relationship between form and
decoration, and an economy of expression, both of
which typify much of Hald's work.

(126) *Vase*
DESIGNED BY MAURICE MARINOT
FRANCE, TROYES      HT. $8\frac{1}{4}''$ (21.0 CM.)
1924      ACC. NO. 51.3.123

Maurice Marinot, originally a painter and a member
of the group "Les Fauves," became interested in and
began to enamel glass in a creative manner in 1910.
Shortly afterwards, he began to design and make his
own glass in the bottle glass factory owned by a
friend in Troyes. His glass is characterized by bold-
ness and massiveness. It was often enhanced by his
ability to make positive use of bubbles and other
defects which would, in other instances, have been
unacceptable in fine glass. He was a forerunner and
leader of Functionalism, or the Art Deco movement,
and his work is considered the epitome of this style.

96

(127)  *Bottle*

Designed by Antonin Daum
France, Nancy, Daum Freres
                                    Ht. 10″ (25.3 cm.)
Ca. 1929                          Acc. No. 72.3.7

Maurice Marinot had a strong influence upon
some of his contemporaries in the 1920's. This
is directly evident in the general conception of
this vase with its thick walls and massive
quality containing inclusions of gold and a
bold, deeply acid-etched design in the surface.

(128)  *"Ala" Plate Signed "Kosta M.
Morales"*

Designed by Mona Morales Schildt
Sweden, Kosta Glassworks
                                    D. 15⅞″ (40.3 cm.)
1970                              Acc. No. 70.3.74

Following the example of Orrefors, other
Scandinavian glasshouses began to hire artists
as designers, resulting in continued Scandinavian leadership in glass design. After World
War II, Scandinavian glassmakers became
noted for their heavy forms of colorless glass,
usually of simple, chaste design. This, in turn,
led to the development and exploitation of
heavy layers of colored glasses. This plate,
with its artful combination of form and color,
exemplifies the best tradition of Swedish glass
of the present day.

(129)  *Air Sculpture Signed "Labino"*

DESIGNED AND EXECUTED BY DOMINICK LABINO

UNITED STATES, GRAND RAPIDS, OHIO    HT. $10\frac{13}{16}''$ (27.5 CM.)

DATED 1969    ACC. NO. 70.4.15

AFTER World War II, a number of craftsmen became interested in using glass as an artistic medium. Sagged, fused, cast, and assembled glass vessels and sculpture resulted, but it was not until 1962 that they began to work directly with hot glass. In that year, what is now called the American Studio Glass Movement was initiated at a workshop at the Toledo Museum of Art. Harvey Littleton, with the technical assistance of Dominick Labino, was chiefly responsible for initiating this new movement. Using small furnaces containing 50-150 pounds of glass, many individual craftsmen are now creatively forming glass and exploring and exploiting the peculiar properties of this material either in their own studios or at universities throughout the country. Glassblowing has become a regular part of the curriculum of some fifty or so universities in this country. The Studio Movement has already exerted a strong effect upon individual glassblowing in England and Europe, and, to a lesser extent, upon decorative glass produced by industry.

# Bibliography

## EARLY TECHNOLOGY

1. AGRICOLA, GEORG. *De Re Metallica*. Basel: Froben and Episcopis, 1556. English edition by Herbert C. Hoover and Lou Henry Hoover. New York: Dover Publications, 1950.

2. BIRINGUCCIO, VANNOCCIO. *De la Pirotechnia* . . . Venezia: Venturino Roffinello, 1540. English edition by Cyril S. Smith and Martha T. Gnudi. New York: American Institute of Mining and Metallurgical Engineers, 1943.

3. HERACLIUS. *Von den Farben und Kunsten der Romer*. Ed. by Albert Ilg. Vol. IV. Wien: Wilhelm Bramuller, 1873.

4. MATTHESIUS, JOHANN. "Die Predig von dem Glassmachen," *Sarepta oder Bergpostill* . . . 15th Sermon. Nurnberg, 1564.

5. NERI, ANTONIO. *L'Arte Vetraria*. Firenze: Giunti, 1612. English edition by Christopher Merret. *The Art of Glass*. London: A. A. for Octavian Pulleyn, 1662. German edition revised and augmented by Johann Kunckel. *Ars Vetraria Experimentalis*. Frankfurt and Leipzig: Johann Bielcke, 1679.

6. PLINIUS SECUNDUS, CAIUS. *Historia Naturalis*. Venezia: Johannes de Spira, 1469. English edition by John Bostock and H. T. Riley. London: H. G. Bohn, 1855-98.

7. THEOPHILUS, called also RUGERUS. *Schedula Diversarum Artium*. Ed. by Albert Ilg. *Quellenschriften fur Kunstgeschichte* . . . Vol. VII. Wien: Wilhelm Bramuller, 1874. English edition by J. G. Hawthorne and C. S. Smith. Chicago: University of Chicago Press, 1963.

## GENERAL

1. BUCKLEY, WILFRED. *European Glass*. Boston: Houghton Mifflin, 1926.

2. BUCKLEY, WILFRED. *The Art of Glass*. New York: The Phaidon Press, 1939.

3. DILLON, EDWARD. *Glass*. London: Methuen and Co., 1907.

4. HAYNES, E. BARRINGTON. *Glass Through the Ages*. London: Penguin Books, 1948.

5. HONEY, WILLIAM B. *Glass, A Handbook for the Study of Glass Vessels of all Periods and Countries* . . . London: Victoria & Albert Museum, 1946.

6. MARIACHER, GIOVANNI. *L'Arte del Vetro*. Verona: Mondadori, 1954.

7. SCHLOSSER, IGNATZ. *Das alte Glas*. Braunschweig: Klinkhardt & Bierman, 1956.

8. SCHMIDT, ROBERT. *Das Glas*. 2nd ed. Berlin-Leipzig: Walter de Gruyter & Co., 1922.

9. VAVRA, JAROSLAV R. *5000 Years of Glass-Making*. Prague: Artia, 1954.

## ANCIENT WORLD

1. BECK, HORACE C. "Glass Before 1500 B.C." *Ancient Egypt and the East*. Part I (June 1934). New York: Macmillan, 1934. 7-21.

2. CORNING MUSEUM OF GLASS, THE. *Glass from the Ancient World. The Ray Winfield Smith Collection*. Corning: The Corning Museum of Glass, 1957.

3. DIMAND, MAURICE S. *A Handbook of Muhammadan Art*. New York: Metropolitan Museum of Art, 1944.

4. DOPPELFELD, OTTO. *Romisches und Frankisches Glas in Koln*. Koln: Greven, 1966.

5. EISEN, GUSTAVUS A. assisted by KOUCHAKJI, FAHIM. *Glass*. 2 Vols. New York: William E. Rudge, 1927.

6. FOSSING, POUL. *Glass Vessels Before Glass-Blowing*. Copenhagen: E. Munksgaard, 1940.

7. FREMERSDORF, FRITZ. *Romische Glaser aus Koln*. Cologne: Verlags-Anstalt und Druckerei, 1928.

8. HARDEN, DONALD B. "Ancient Glass, I: Pre-Roman." *The Archaeological Journal*, CXXV (1969), 46-72.

9. HARDEN, DONALD B. "Ancient Glass, II: Roman." *The Archaeological Journal*, CXXVI (1970), 44-77.

10. HARDEN, DONALD B. "Ancient Glass, III: Post Roman." *The Archae-ological Journal*, CXXVIII (1972), 78-117.

11. HARDEN, DONALD B.; PAINTER, K. S.; PINDER-WILSON, R. H.; and TAIT, HUGH. *Masterpieces of Glass*. London: Trustees of the British Museum, 1968.

12. HARDEN, DONALD B. *Roman Glass from Karanis*. Ann Arbor: University of Michigan Press, 1936.

13. ISINGS, CLASINA. *Roman Glass from Dated Finds*. Groningen: Djakarta, J. B. Wolters, 1957.

14. KISA, ANTON. *Das Glas im Altertume*. 3 vols. Leipzig: K. W. Hiersemann, 1908.

15. LAMM, CARL J. *Glass from Iran in the National Museum, Stockholm*. Stockholm: C. E. Fritze, 1935.

16. LAMM, CARL J. "Glass and Hard Stone Vessels." in POPE, A. U. *A Survey of Persian Art . . .* London, 1939. Vol. III, 2592-2606; Vol. VI, 1438-1455.

17. LAMM, CARL J. *Mittelalterliche Glaser und Steinschnittarbeiten aus dem Nahen Osten*. 2 vols. Berlin: D. Reimer, 1930.

18. MORIN-JEAN. *La Verrerie en Gaule sous l'Empire Romain*. Paris: H. Laurens, 1913.

19. NEUBERG, FREDERIC. *Antikes Glas*. Darmstadt: Eduard Roether Verlag, 1962.

20. OPPENHEIM, A. LEO; BRILL, ROBERT H.; BARAG, DAN; and VON SALDERN, AXEL. *Glass and Glassmaking in Ancient Mesopotamia*. Corning: The Corning Museum of Glass, 1970.

21. RICHTER, GISELA M. A. *The Room of Ancient Glass*. New York: The Metropolitan Museum of Art, 1930.

22. RIEFSTAHL, ELIZABETH. *Ancient Egyptian Glass and Glazes in The Brooklyn Museum*. Brooklyn: The Brooklyn Museum, 1968.

23. SCHMORANZ, GUSTAV. *Old Oriental Gilt and Enameled Glass Vessels*. Vienna and London: Osterreichisches Handels Museum, 1899.

24. TROWBRIDGE, MARY LUELLA. *Philological Studies in Ancient Glass*. Urbana: University of Illinois Press, 1930.

25. WIET, GASTON. *Lampes et Bouteilles en Verre Emaillé*. Cairo: Museum of Islamic Art, 1929.

## MIDDLE AGES

1. HARDEN, DONALD B. "Glass Vessels in Britain and Ireland, A.D. 400-1000." *Dark Age Britain*. London: Methuen and Co., 1956. 132-167.

2. RADEMACHER, FRANZ. *Die Deutschen Glaser des Mittelalters*. Berlin: Verlag fur Kunstwissenschaft, 1933.

3. RADEMACHER, FRANZ. "Frankische Glaser aus dem Rheinland." *Bonner Jahrbucher*. Vol. 147 (1942). 285-344.


## EUROPE

1. BARRELET, JAMES. *La Verrerie en France* . . . Paris: Libraire Larousse, 1953.

2. CHAMBON, RAYMOND. *L'Histoire de la Verrerie en Belgique*. Bruxelles: Librarie Encyclopédique, 1955.

3. FROTHERINGHAM, ALICE WILSON. *Spanish Glass*. New York: Thomas Yoseloff, 1964.

4. GASPARETTO, ASTONE. *Il Vetro di Murano dalle Origini ad Oggi*. Venice: Neri Pozza Editore, 1958.

5. GELDER, H. E. VAN. *Glas en Ceramiek*. Utrecht: W. de Haan, 1955.

6. MARIACHER, GIOVANNI. *Italian Blown Glass from Ancient Rome to Venice*. New York, London, Toronto: McGraw Hill, 1961.

7. PAZAUREK, GUSTAV E. *Glaser der Empire und Biedermeierzeit*. Leipzig: Klinkhardt and Biermann, 1923.

8. PAZAUREK, GUSTAV E. *Moderne Glaser*. Leipzig: Hermann Seemann Nachfolger, 1901.

9. POLAK, ADA BUCH. *Gammelt Norsk Glass*. Oslo: Gyldendal Norsk Forlag, 1953.

10. POLAK, ADA BUCH. *Modern Glass*. New York: Thomas Yoseloff, 1962.

11. REVI, ALBERT CHRISTIAN. *Nineteenth Century Glass, Its Genesis and Development*. New York: Thomas Nelson & Sons, 1959.

12. SALDERN, AXEL VON. *German Enameled Glass*. Corning: The Corning Museum of Glass, 1965.

13. SCHMIDT, ROBERT. *Brandenburgische Glaser*. Berlin: Verlag fur Kunstwissenschaft, 1914.

14. SCHMIDT, ROBERT. *Die Glaser der Sammlung Muhsam.* 2 Vols. Berlin: Verlag fur Kunstwissenschaft, 1914 and 1926.

15. SEITZ, HERIBERT. *Aldre Svenska Glas.* Stockholm: Nordiska Museets Handlinger, 1936.


## ENGLAND AND IRELAND

1. BUCKLEY, FRANCIS. *A History of Old English Glass.* London: E. Benn, 1925.

2. CHURCHILL, ARTHUR, LTD. *History in Glass.* London: Arthur Churchill, Ltd., 1937.

3. FLEMING, JOHN ARNOLD. *Scottish and Jacobite Glass.* Glasgow: Jackson, Son and Co., 1938.

4. GUTTERY, D. R. *From Broad-Glass to Cut Crystal.* London: Leonard Hill, 1956.

5. HARTSHORNE, ALBERT. *Old English Glasses.* London and New York: E. Arnold, 1897.

6. HUGHES, G. BERNARD. *English, Scottish and Irish Table Glass . . .* London: B. T. Batsford, 1956.

7. PELLATT, APSLEY. *Curiosities of Glassmaking.* London: David Bogue, 1849.

8. POWELL, HARRY J. *Glassmaking in England.* Cambridge: University Press, 1923.

9. THORPE, W. A. *English Glass,* 3rd edition. London: A. & C. Black, 1961.

10. THORPE, W. A. *A History of English and Irish Glass.* 2 Vols. London: The Medici Society, 1929.

11. WAKEFIELD, HUGH. *Nineteenth Century British Glass.* London: Faber and Faber, 1961.

12. WARREN, PHELPS. *Irish Glass: The Age of Exuberance.* London: Faber and Faber, 1970.

13. WESTROPP, M. S. DUDLEY. *Irish Glass.* London: H. Jenkins, 1920.

104

# UNITED STATES

1. INNES, LOWELL. *Early Glass of the Pittsburgh District, 1797-1890.* Pittsburgh: Carnegie Museum, 1949.

2. LEE, RUTH WEBB. *Handbook of Early American Pressed Glass Patterns.* Wellesley Hills, Mass.: Lee Publications, 1964.

3. LEE, RUTH WEBB, and ROSE, JAMES H. *American Glass Cup Plates.* Wellesley Hills, Mass.: Lee Publications, 1948.

4. McKEARIN, GEORGE S., and HELEN. *American Glass.* New York: Crown Publishers, 1948.

5. McKEARIN, HELEN. *The Story of American Historical Flasks.* Corning: The Corning Museum of Glass, 1953.

6. McKEARIN, HELEN, and GEORGE S. *Two Hundred Years of American Blown Glass.* Garden City, N. Y.: Doubleday, 1950.

7. REVI, ALBERT CHRISTIAN. *American Art Nouveau Glass.* Camden, N. J.: Thomas Nelson & Sons, 1968.

8. REVI, ALBERT CHRISTIAN. *American Cut and Engraved Glass.* New York: Thomas Nelson & Sons, 1965.

9. REVI, ALBERT CHRISTIAN. *Nineteenth Century Art Glass.* 2nd ed. New York: Thomas Nelson & Sons, 1959.

10. ROSE, JAMES H. *The Story of American Pressed Glass of the Lacy Period, 1825-1850.* Corning: The Corning Museum of Glass, 1954.

11. WILSON, KENNETH M. *New England Glass & Glassmaking.* New York: Thomas Y. Crowell Co., 1972.

# FAR EAST

1. BLAIR, DOROTHY. *A History of Glass in Japan.* Tokyo: Kodansha International Ltd. and The Corning Museum of Glass, 1973.

2. HONEY, WILLIAM B. "Chinese Glass." *Transactions of the Oriental Ceramic Society*, Vol. 17, 1939/40. 35-47.

3. HONEY, WILLIAM B. "Early Chinese Glass" *Burlington Magazine*, Vol. LXXI, No. 416, (Nov. 1937). 211-222.

4. SELIGMAN, C. G., and BECK, H. C. *Far Eastern Glass: Some Western Origins.* Stockholm, 1938. Reprinted from *The Bulletin of the Museum of Far Eastern Antiquities*, No. 10.

# Index